Written by:
Joanne Currah
Jane Felling

1st Printing March 2001

"Box Cars" won the National Learning Disabilities Association Idea of the Year 1991.

ISBN: **0-9681613-9-1**

IN DEDICATION
TO OUR ANGEL

This book is for our angel, Shannon Marie Langlois.
We will always remember your
vibrant spirit and love for life.

In our formative years of teaching, Shannon
encouraged both of us to become teachers who were willing
to take risks and "play" right along with our students.

Thank you Shannon for keeping us true to ourselves and
helping us learn how to teach and "learn" how to learn.

You will always be in our hearts.

Jane and Joanne

TABLE OF CONTENTS

Place Value and Probability

GAME	LEVEL	SKILLS	PAGE
Deca Train (TP)	K - 2	building 10's, number recognition, probability	34
Deca Train Challenger (TP)	1 - 3	building 10's and 1's, rounding, probability, adding	37
Decadice Line Up (TP)	K - 3	ordering 10's	39
Decagraphic (TP)	K - 3	recognizing and naming decades, graphing, interpreting bar graphs	41
Decagraphic II (TP)	2 - 4	adding 10's and 1's, rounding to 10's, interpreting bar graphs	43
Rolling A "Round" (TP)	3 - 6	adding 10's and 1's, rounding to 10's, data analysis, probability	44
Detective Line Up (TP)	3 - 6	ordering numbers, identifying and analyzing patterns	47
Tweenies (TP)	1 - 3	comparing numbers 0 - 90	50
Tweenies Variation (TP)	4 - 6	comparing numbers 0 - 9 090	50
Chip Tac Toe (TP)	1 - 3	learning numbers on a 100 board	57
Ten For Me	2 - 4	adding, patterning, place value, learning numbers on a 100 board	58
Treasure Hunt (TP)	1 - 3	>, <, odd, even, logical reasoning	61
Treasure Hunt Variation (TP)	4 - 6	>, <, odd, even, logical reasoning, factors, multiples	61
In the Zone (Snap)	2 - 5	comparing numbers 0 - 90, reading numbers	63
In the Zone Variation (Non-Snap)	1 - 3	comparing numbers 0 - 90, money	64
Deck Ya	1 - 3	comparing numbers 0 - 90	66
Pondering Predictions	1 - 3	comparing numbers 0 - 90, >, <, odd, even	69

* (TP) Thought Provokers have been itemized for your reference.

Place Value and Probability (continued)

* (TP) Thought Provokers have been itemized for your reference.

The Operations

* (TP) Thought Provokers have been itemized for your reference.

The Operations (continued)

Fractions, Money & More

* (TP) Thought Provokers have been itemized for your reference.

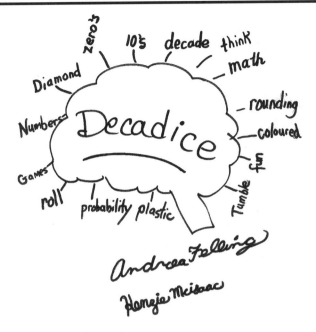

Andrea Felling

Hanjia Mcisaac

Decadice

They're really nice
They make you think twice
So let me give you some great advice
When in doubt... roll decadice!

By Mackenzie

Introduction

INTRODUCTION

It has been three years since our last publication. Over this period we have met hundreds of teachers at conferences and in our workshops who ask "When is your next book coming out?" To be honest our writing pace had been hectic since 1990 with approximately two books a year coming out. As workshop demands increased we took a needed break from writing.

In late 1999 and early 2000, the requests for new material increased. We didn't want to publish just another book. We wanted our new book to reflect how we had grown and changed as game creators. More importantly, we wanted it to reflect the significant way in which we have changed while working with students. To this end, we hope you will see a qualitative shift in our writing. The book is filled with "Thought Provokers" which are great questions that will help you "dig under the fun" and extend mathematical learning. Teaching Tips are scattered throughout to help you maximize the game activities for the kids. We've also included many classroom samples from eager students who taught us so much and these samples will provide you with starting points for your own students.

Where do our ideas come from? Our primary source of inspiration comes from volunteering in our own childrens' classrooms. Secondly, the ideas were generated from the unique properties of the decadice. We've been playing with these dice for approximately two years. Over this time, scrap pieces of paper filled with game ideas began to accumulate and were literally sitting in the bottom of our briefcases (scary!). It became inevitable that it was time to refocus and revisit our writing process.

We are often asked how we write and generate our ideas. We write, invent and test out our ideas totally independent of one another over a period of time (in this case two years). Then the fun begins! We leave the office and head out to our favorite coffee houses, away from phones and other distractions. We play and share our games, sometimes receiving the strangest of looks from passers-by. What is exciting, is that we usually discover how diverse and unique each other's work has been. Then it is a matter of writing, testing, editing and more editing! We affectionately call this the "my brain is hurting phase" and we bribe ourselves with good coffee and a run in the river valley just to get it done. Writing this latest volume has been what we needed after three hectic years of family life and Box Cars.

We sincerely hope you enjoy using our newest book as much as we enjoyed creating it.

Jane and Joanne

THE BOX CARS AND ONE-EYED JACKS PHILOSOPHY

The Box Cars and One-Eyed Jacks series of books promote the use of games using cards, dice and multi-sided dice to teach mathematics and language. Starting with a very simple concept ten years ago, the series has evolved to encompass much more than "having fun with games" to practice basic math and language.

From day one, we had a strong vision about children learning through games. After ten years we are continuing to work towards our vision but are now able to express it more clearly. We've learned, and are continuing to learn about why games work.

1. Children are naturally intrigued and captivated by math games. Whether a game is simple or complex, the highly motivating materials of cards, dice and multi-sided dice attract and hold a learner's attention.

2. Games fit the research that indicates brief, engaging, purposeful practice is a powerful strategy for developing understanding and mastery of basic concepts. Games can be easily changed and manipulated to suit the needs of the learner and the teaching objective. All students play, but with many variations students are able to respond at different levels and in different ways to an activity.

3. Games allow children to work in a non-threatening atmosphere towards mastery of concepts. When motivating, challenging, problem solving activities are integrated into games, children are able to learn as they are developmentally ready. By using games, teachers can capitalize on childrens' innate desire to play and learn through play. If the atmosphere is positive and flexible, students are more likely to learn.

4. Games can engage learners in a cycle of mathematical thinking. As they play a math game children:

> a) formulate questions.
>
> b) create strategies.
>
> c) will often use an unsophisticated "it seems to work" method. Success is a result of experimenting with this trial and error approach.
>
> d) adopt a strategy for methods that work consistently over time.

This type of activity requires the learner to use critical thinking and logical reasoning as they analyze and become aware of their strategies. Making sense of mathematical ideas, acquiring skills and solving problems is at the very heart of mathematics. Good thought provoking games allow children the opportunity to get there.

5. Games can provide an excellent experience for learners to write about mathematics and their learning. As they develop and analyze their strategies they must clarify their thinking in order to share their ideas with others. Writing responses to game activities helps many students reach this understanding and apply reasoning processes to similar situations. The learner realizes the value of these experiences as they can transfer their knowledge to other related experiences. As children play they naturally converse. There are ample opportunities for teachers to informally assess a student's understanding by "playing alongside", observing, or having them demonstrate the game. This first hand assessment leads to further instruction.

6. Our math games are multi-sensory and accommodate all learning styles. The cards and dice are tactile and are used as true math manipulatives. Cards and dice are extremely visual with predictable patterns. Learners constantly "talk the math" as they play and/or re-teach, making games auditory and socially interactive in nature. For some children, the physical component of active learning is key to transferring their knowledge to other related experiences (i.e. real-life situations).

In conclusion,

> If math is a game, then respect and challenge its power and potential as a teaching strategy for effective learning!
>
> Roll the dice, deal the cards and get playing. Everybody WINS!

HOW TO USE THIS BOOK

Decadice begins with extensive sections on teaching place value, graphing, data management and rounding strategies. Excellent whole class warm up activities have been provided in one section for you to use as a quick reference.

Decadice contains 69 games. The games are divided into the following sections:

1. Place Value and Probability

2. The Operations

3. Fractions, Money & More

Within each section the games are organized using the following format:

LEVEL: This is the appropriate grade level (suggested only). It is intended to be flexible.

SKILLS: Specific math skills are listed here.

EQUIPMENT: Specific items are listed including which card values are needed. An ace is given the value of 1 in all of our games - indicated (Ace = 1) in the instructions. We use the Kings as 0's. Counters should always be made available for the students who need them. If a reproducible is needed it will be indicated in the rules and found at the back of the book. Keep in mind that students may be able to simply copy the gameboard in their Box Cars book or math book to save on photocopying.

GETTING STARTED: These are the rules and instructions which can be changed to meet the various levels within the classroom.

VARIATIONS: Variations are ideas to increase or decrease difficulty, or to extend the concept and add new skills.

TEACHING TIPS & THOUGHT PROVOKERS:

The biggest change in this volume is the number of games that include Teaching Tips and Thought Provokers. Games that include Thought Provokers are indicated with "(TP)" in the Table of Contents.

The Teaching Tips will provide specific suggestions for teaching a strategy or concept within the context of that game. It is advisable to read through the entire game prior to playing, as in some instances the Teaching Tips are best done before the game is introduced.

THOUGHT PROVOKER GAMES

We selected what we considered to be our best games where the "play" experience can lead to excellent mathematical extensions and writing opportunities. Students should be allowed "more than a one shot play" of the game. We suggest the following format for Thought Provoker Games.

1) Day One of the Game: 45 - 60 minutes are necessary to introduce the game rules and allow for a sufficient play period. If the game includes Thought Provokers, these should be read and discussed prior to playing. During the last 15 minutes, have students share their developing strategies in a guided discussion.

2) Throughout the week, allow students to have follow up play periods during free time (this could even be at recess: approximately 20 minutes). Encourage and organize opportunities for students to play the games at home. Having students re-teach the game rules to other family members is very effective for reinforcing concepts.

3) The following week, lead a class discussion about the game. Have students share their responses and strategies. Allow time for students to follow up and write their responses to the Thought Provokers (if this was not completed during the week).

It is our experience that encouraging children to verbalize their ideas to others enhances their written work and understanding. Communicating their strategies and experiences, helps to clarify what they put down on paper. Build in sharing time in the math class to maximize success in writing the Thought Provokers on Day One, as they are introduced to the game. Knowing ahead of time what they will be writing about helps focus their play. We tell them it gets their "brains ready to look for and experience the math they have to write about". Providing the questions ahead of time also allows the teacher to focus their own observations as they circulate in the classroom. We will often catch students verbalizing answers to some of the questions and we reinforce this learning by confirming, "You're on the right track."

The games do not have to be played in any set order. Teachers and parents can select games to introduce a concept or skill, practice a concept or skill (see Math Warm-Ups section) or master a concept or skill.

The rules and instructions for all games are meant to be flexible. We encourage you and your students to change the equipment, skills or rules. As you play more of the games, you will discover how easy it is to change and re-invent during the game playing process. Many of the games in Decadice were created in just this way.

The front section also includes ideas for teaching place value, rounding strategies and graphing/data management. As we reworked these games with our "assistants" we realized the incredible potential for extending the learning for these concepts.

PRACTICING PLACE VALUE
WITH THE DECADICE AND OTHER MANIPULATIVES

LEVEL: Kindergarten - Grade 3

SKILLS: Practicing building 10's and 1's, adding and subtracting with regrouping

EQUIPMENT: decadice, regular dice, base ten manipulative (i.e. interlocking cubes), place value mat

Some Simple Activities For Beginners:

1) Roll a decadie:

Now build that number and verbalize its value (e.g. "sixty").

2) Roll a decadie and a regular die:

Now build that number and verbalize its value (e.g. "seventy four").

3) Step One: Roll a decadie: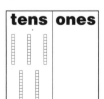

Now build that number.

xiv

Step Two: Roll the regular die or ten-sided (0-9) die and subtract that number from the "tens" number (in the diagram below, the player rolls a 6).

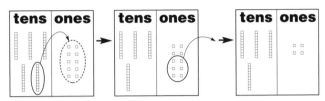

Change one ten into ten ones and then subtract six ones (50 - 6 = 44).

4) Both players start with 0. Each player in turn rolls a ten-sided die or regular die and the first to reach 100 wins.

5) Players start at 100. Now players roll regular dice or ten-sided dice, subtracting down to 0.

6) Place Value Face Offs: Both players have a place value mat. Each player rolls a decadie plus a regular die. Players build and compare. The greatest number wins (like war!).

Player One rolls:

tens	ones

= 42

Player Two rolls: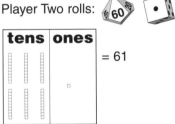

tens	ones

= 61

Player Two verbalizes, "sixty one is greater than forty two."

7) Adding Face Offs: Players roll their decadie and regular die or ten-sided (0-9) die twice per turn and add them for the greatest sum.

Player One   Player Two

28 + 64 = 92   55 + 32 = 87

Player One verbalizes, "Ninety two is greater than eighty seven."

8) Subtracting Face Offs: Players roll the decadie and regular die or ten-sided (0-9) die. Players subtract the regular or ten-sided die from the decadie. The least difference wins.

Player One   Player Two

40 - 2 = 38   60 - 9 = 51

38 is less than 51 so Player One earns a point.

NOTE: For both the above examples, continue to have students use place value manipulatives and charts.

GRAPHING AND DATA MANAGEMENT ACTIVITIES

Throughout the writing of this book, testing the games and working with the students, data management activities became a natural extension of the play. There are many opportunities to develop these skills when playing the Decadice games. The ability to construct, read, analyze and interpret graphs is an important skill. We have outlined the type of graphing opportunities that are possible and highlighted the most suitable games in the book that go with each. Many student samples have been provided as a guideline for you.

1. BAR GRAPHS

These types of graphs are used mainly for comparing similar data. Bars are typically displayed vertically, but may also be shown horizontally. Bars are of equal width.

2. MULTIPLE BAR GRAPHS

A bar graph that combines two bar graphs. These types of graphs are used mainly for comparing similar data from related groups. The bars may be grouped together depending on the purpose.

SEE: "Rolling Around" on page 44.

3. LINE PLOT OR VERTICAL LINE GRAPHS

This type of graph is often confused with a bar graph but it shows each piece of data. It shows the relative size and frequency of numbers (i.e. the spread of the data). All pieces of information are represented. You can easily identify the range and mode.

SEE: "Deca Train" on page 34.

4. CIRCLE OR PIE GRAPHS

This type of graph is used when comparing data to the whole and different parts of the whole. Each fraction or piece of the "pie" represents a proportionate part of the whole.

SEE: "The Range Game" on page 70.

5. HISTOGRAM

Histograms are useful for displaying the frequency in which events occur. The data is displayed in a series of bars of the same width, not separated by a space to show that as one set of data ends, the next one begins. The scale on the horizontal axis is usually represented by a range.

SEE: "Decagraphic" and "Decagraphic II" on pages 41 and 43.

6. STEM AND LEAF PLOTS

Stem and leaf plots allow you to organize numbers in your data so that the numbers make the display. They are effective tools for showing the concentration of numbers when there is a large set of data.

SEE: "Decade Duel" on page 78.

Choose stem (in this case a digit in the 10's place) and plot using a vertical number line. The data is then graphed on the leaf side (in this case a digit in the one's place).

We found that many of the games lent themselves to the study of mean, median and mode. Even younger students learned these statistical concepts with practical understanding, through the games.

The three main ways to describe a set of numbers are mean, median and mode.

MEAN: The average value found by adding the numbers in a set and then dividing the sum by how many are in the set. For example, 38 is the mean for the set of numbers 30, 40 and 44; $(30 + 40 + 44) \div 3 = 38$. This works best for sets of data where there are no really high or low numbers.

SEE: "Tweenies" on page 50, "Football Factor" on page 161 and "100 000 Aire" on page 142.

MEDIAN: The middle number or value when values are arranged in ascending or descending order. For example, 11 is the median for the set of numbers 6, 10, 11, 20 and 42. This works best for sets of data where a couple pieces of data are much higher or lower than most of the other data.

SEE: "Football Factor" on page 161 and "100 000 Aire" on page 142.

MODE: The number that occurs most often in a set of numbers. Graphing activities using line plots (see "Deca Train") and tallying activities lend themselves to looking at the mode. These work best with sets containing many identical pieces of data.

SEE: "Deca Train" on page 34 and "100 000 Aire" on page 142.

TALLY CHARTS: A tally chart uses stroke marks to record the frequency of data as follows: $||||= 4$ $\cancel{||||} = 5$

Tallies are most useful when you're counting events as they happen. Tallying is an important skill to teach as once data has been tallied it can be sorted into frequency charts and then graphed, analyzed and compared. It is a way for students to easily count large samples.

SEE: "Decagraphic" on page 41.

ROUNDING STRATEGIES AND TIPS

Many of our games involve rounding practice. We have used the following strategies in grade 2 through grade 8 classrooms. We have experienced first hand just how much students needed this assistance. Teachers confirm that students require a lot of opportunity to practice!

You will find that both decadice and ten-sided dice are perfect for rounding activities and practice.

We started by teaching the basic rules for rounding as outlined in the chart below:

To round to the nearest 10:	To round to the nearest 100:	To round to the nearest 1000:	To round to the nearest 10 000:	To round to the nearest 100 000:
If the ones digit is 5 or greater round up to the next 10. If it is less than 5 round down.	If the tens digit is 5 or greater round up to the next 100. If it is less than 5 round down.	If the hundreds digit is 5 or greater round up to the next 1000. If it is less than 5 round down.	If the thousands digit is 5 or greater round up to the next 10 000. If it is less than 5 round down.	If the ten thousands digit is 5 or greater round up to the next 100 000. If it is less than 5 round down.
1 376 rounds to 1 380 4 591 rounds to 4 590	4 878 rounds to 4 900 8 347 rounds to 8 300	5 681 rounds to 6 000 7 395 rounds to 7 000	18 274 rounds to 20 000 62 499 rounds to 60 000	142 391 rounds to 100 000 367 890 rounds to 400 000

We realized we had to add to this chart by teaching 'directly':

If the number you are rounding ends in 0, 1, 2, 3 or 4, that's a "stay-put" number. The place value position you are rounding "stays-put" (you'll see what we mean in our example).

If the number you are rounding ends in a 5, 6, 7, 8 or 9, that is a "round up" number. The place value position you are rounding BUMPS UP by one.

We practice these basic rules with the ten-sided (0-9) die. It is perfect for practicing basic rounding rules as it is numbered 0 through 9 and has all rounding possibilities on it.

Have students warm up for any of the rounding games by rolling the die, identifying the number and stating whether it is a "round up" or "stay put" number.

As we observed students play the rounding games we noticed that part of the difficulty they experienced when rounding numbers was identifying what place value holder to look at for rounding to the nearest 10, 100, 1 000, etc.

We found two things that really helped:

1) labeling or marking the place value position on a reproducible gameboard prior to rounding (see pages 213, 214, 215 and 216).

2) providing a number line of rounded numbers for a visual reference.

The following visual examples come from "Flippin' Out" on page 86.

A visual number line helped many students locate their numbers and practice the "stay put" or "round up" strategy.

Example:

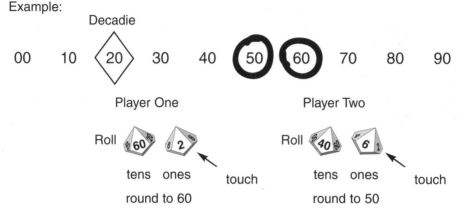

Decadie

00   10   ⟨20⟩   30   40   (50) (60) 70   80   90

Player One   Player Two

Roll 60 2   Roll 40 6

tens ones   touch   tens ones   touch

round to 60   round to 50

Players would touch the ones number and identify it as a "round up" or "stay put" number. In the above example, Player One says, "Two is a stay put number." Therefore, Player One rounds to 6 tens (60). Player One would then put a bingo chip on 60. Their opponent (who rolled 46) would touch 6, which is a "round up" number. They would then bump up 4 tens to 5 tens, thus rounding to 50. Player Two would then put a bingo chip on 50.

In "Flippin' Out" the decadie is rolled to determine which player has the rounded number closest to the target. We encourage students to put this target roll right on their number line as well, so that players can visually see who is "closest to" the target. In the example above, the target is 20. Since Player Two's roll is closer to the target, Player Two wins.

When building larger numbers we use the same techniques, always starting with the process outlined above.

For instance, to round to the nearest hundred, we change the number line for visual reference to:

000	100	200	300	400	500	600	700	800	900	1 000

It is now necessary to turn over three cards when creating numbers into the hundreds place.

Rounding to the nearest 100, we touch the <u>tens</u> place value, determine if it's a "round up" or "stay put" number and apply our rules. We directly teach "when rounding to the nearest '____', look one place value position to the right, and then apply your strategy."

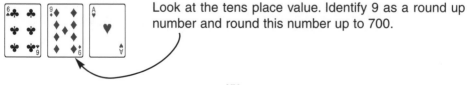

Look at the tens place value. Identify 9 as a round up number and round this number up to 700.

We have included several reproducible gameboards for the students to use for practice. See the following games for rounding. We think you'll be amazed at how quickly your students' skills will improve!

Decagraphic II   Rolling A Round   Double Round Up
Flippin' Out   Flippin' Out Variations Double Round Up Variations
Figure Eight   A Target Round   A Target Round Variations

One final observation that we'd like to share:

We noticed some common errors that students incur when rounding larger numbers.

For example: 768 028 rounded to the nearest 100 000's

Students would apply their rule but hold onto some of the original digit as follows:

800 0<u>28</u>

We used this phrase which seemed to help students complete the rounding process. Identify the proper place value, apply your rules for rounding, then:

"Round it ____ then zero the rest of it out".

e.g. 800 000

"Round it up then zero the rest of it out!"

For some, it may be helpful to play a variety of games at different degrees of difficulty. The students who did experience some confusion initially, shared with us that the practice and teaching tips took the "mystery" out of rounding. So give it a try!

Quick Math
Warm-Ups

QUICK MATH WARM UPS
EXERCISE YOUR BRAIN!

These quick, easy to do warm up ideas are based upon some of our original WARS/SNAPS and MENTAL MATH activities from our first three books.

The ideas will work best when starting off or ending your math class. Designed for whole class participation, they'll get your math class ROLLING. Remember, as students are playing, observe and informally evaluate or just play right along. The Warm Ups are written to use the decadice alone or in combination with regular and ten-sided (0-9) dice. Cards can be substituted for the regular and ten-side dice. Cards are especially effective for students who still need to have manipulatives for adding and subtracting.

1. Roll a die and count forward using a 10's pattern, three in sequence. For example, roll 20 and say, "30, 40, 50."

2. Roll a die and count backward using a 10's pattern, three in sequence (if possible). For example, roll 70 and say, "60, 50, 40."

3. Roll a die and double it (e.g. Roll 60 + 60 = 120). At a higher level, roll, double and add 10 (e.g. 60 + 60 + 10 = 130). For more practice, roll, double it and multiply by 10 (e.g. (60 + 60) x 10 = 1 200). For a variation, roll the die and divide it in half (e.g. Roll 90 ÷ 2 = 45).

4. Roll a die and multiply by 10, 100 or 1 000 (e.g. Roll 4 x 10 = 40, 4 x 100 = 400 or 4 x 1 000 = 4 000).

WARS AND VARIATIONS

Number War between two players:

Player One rolls 20
Player Two rolls 40

Player Two says, "40 is greater than 20." and earns a point. In the event of a tie, both players earn a point.

VARIATION #1: Roll two decadice and add them before determining the winner.

Player One rolls 20 + 30 = 50
Player Two rolls 40 + 00 = 40

Player One says, "50 is a greater sum than 40" and earns a point.

VARIATION #2: Roll two decadice and subtract one from the other before determining the winner (least difference wins).

Player One rolls 30 - 20 = 10
Player Two rolls 50 - 20 = 30

Player One says, "10 is the least difference" and earns a point.

VARIATION #3: Roll two decadice and a ten-sided (0-9) die and add them before determining the winner.

Player One rolls 40 + 10 + 5 = 55
Player Two rolls 20 + 60 + 9 = 89

Player Two says, "89 is a greater sum than 55" and earns a point.

VARIATION #4: Roll two decadice and multiply them before determining the winner.

Player One rolls 10 x 30 = 300
Player Two rolls 40 x 80 = 3 200

Player Two says, "3 200 is a greater product than 300" and earns a point.

SNAPS AND VARIATIONS

1. Adding Snap - This involves mentally adding 10's to 180. At the same time players roll one decadie each. Players add these numbers together and the first player to call out the correct sum earns 1 point. For example, Player One rolls 40 and Player Two rolls 60. The first player to verbalize, "100" earns a point. If players call out the correct answer at the same time, then no one earns a point.

2. Subtraction/Multiplication Snap - Play with the same rules as adding snap but use subtraction (subtracting 10's from 90) or multiplication (multiplying by 10's numbers to 8 100).

3. Three Addend Snap - Players roll three decadice and add these together. The first player to call out the correct sum earns 1 point. This is a great activity for practicing "doubles", "doubles + 1" and "hunting for a 10" methods.

    e.g. 60 + 60 + 20 = 120 + 20 = 140 OR 60 + 40 + 50 = 100 + 50 = 150

4. Reduce Fraction Snap - Each player rolls one decadie. Both players mentally build a proper fraction and reduce it to its simplest terms (if possible). If a player rolls 00 it must be re-rolled. The first player to call out the fraction in its reduced form earns 1 point.

    e.g. 20/80 = "one-fourth" and 30/90 = "one-third"

ADDING FACE OFFS

Each player rolls two decadice and two regular dice per turn, and adds and compares them for the greatest sum.

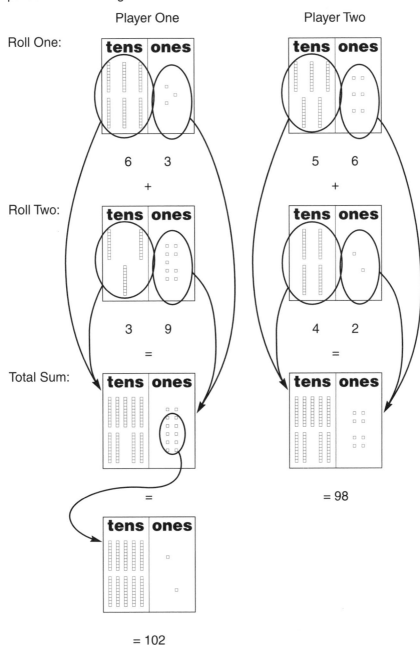

Player One

Roll One:

tens	ones

6   3

+

Roll Two:

tens	ones

3   9

=

Total Sum:

tens	ones

=

tens	ones

= 102

Player Two

Roll One:

tens	ones

5   6

+

Roll Two:

tens	ones

4   2

=

tens	ones

= 98

SUBTRACTING FACE OFFS

STEP ONE: Each player rolls two decadice and builds their tens.

Player One	Player Two
Rolls: 20 + 40	Rolls: 60 + 10
Builds: 6 tens	Builds: 7 tens

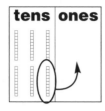

STEP TWO: Each player now rolls their ten-sided (0-9) die to determine how many ones they need to subtract.

Player One	Player Two
Rolls: 4	Rolls: 9

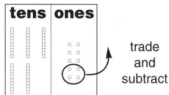

trade
and
subtract

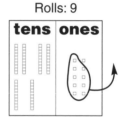

STEP THREE: Players calculate their answers.

60 - 4 = 56   70 - 9 = 61

Player One verbalizes, "56 is less than 61." and earns a point.

WARM-UPS USING DECADICE AND
REGULAR OR TEN-SIDED (0-9) DICE

Adding 10's and 1's: Roll one decadie and one regular die to practice adding 10's and 1's.

e.g.

6 tens + 4 ones = sixty four
"Sixty plus four equals sixty four."

Players can roll on a place value mat.

Tens	Ones

Play against an opponent and follow the rules for Number War.

Subtracting 10's and 1's: Roll one decadie and a regular die to practice subtracting from 10's.

e.g.

7 tens - 5 ones = 65
"Seventy minus five equals sixty five."

Players will have to verbalize and count back to find their answer. Play against an opponent and follow the rules for Number War. Remember, the least difference wins for subtraction.

Place Value
and Probability

PONDERING PROBABILITY

The games in this section are ideal for exploring probability concepts. The games can engage students in a cycle of:

1. Collecting and representing data.

2. Summarizing, comparing and interpreting data.

3. Data analysis including:

- formulating questions.

- deciding whether the data gives them enough information to answer questions.

- describing events as:

- likely/unlikely

- probable/improbable

- certain, impossible, equally likely

- developing and evaluating inferences and predictions for future events based on data.

4. Conducting probability experiments using games to:

- investigate the likelihood of events.

- learn how to quantify the likelihood of events (middle years).

- predict the frequency of outcomes and develop outcome charts.

- explain results.

#3 and #4 often go hand in hand. As students reflect on the game and the generated data they usually discover the best way to organize and display data in a meaningful format.

PROBABILITY GAME

- Evaluate
- New Prediction **5**

1 Predict

The Games Cycle Lets You Explore Probability in a Meaningful Context.

- Discuss **4**
- Summarize
- Reflect
- Interpret Data

2 Play
- Formulate Strategies
- Gather Data

3
- Organize Results
- Display

DECA TRAIN

LEVEL: Kindergarten - Grade 2

SKILLS: Building 10's, number recognition, probability (grades 1 and 2)

PLAYERS: 2 - 4

EQUIPMENT: One decadie per player, one gameboard (see reproducibles), pencil

GETTING STARTED: Each player has their own gameboard.

Before play, have players predict how many rolls it will take to cross off all of the numbers on their "deca train".

Player One begins by rolling one decadie and verbalizing that number out loud. Player One then crosses this number off their "deca train".

EXAMPLE: Player One rolls 50 and crosses it off.

Players alternate rolling and crossing off the corresponding number on their "deca train". If a number rolled has already been crossed off (i.e. eliminated), then that player misses their turn. The first player to cross off all their numbers is the winner. Have players predict how many rolls they think it will take to cross off all of the numbers on their train.

00
10
20
30
40
50
60
70
80
90

VARIATION: **Solitaire Version**

If players prefer to play solo, they could add three "X's" underneath their gameboard and circle one "X" every time they can't remove a number. After three "X's" (strikes) have been circled the game ends and you're OUT!

TEACHING TIP: Make interlocking cubes available and have children build the number rolled. This reinforces the concept that ten "ones" equals one "ten".

EXAMPLE:　　　　Roll a 20 and player builds:

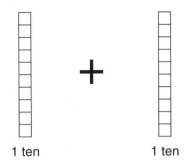

1 ten　　　　　　　1 ten

= 2 tens or 20

 TEACHING TIP:　After all students have completed at least one round of play, have them record and create a class graph indicating the numbers of rolls it took to cross off all their numbers.

THOUGHT PROVOKERS:

1. How many rolls did it take to cross off all your numbers? How did this compare to your prediction?

2. Look at the class graph. What was the most frequent number of rolls needed to cross off all the numbers?

BONUS BRAIN BOOSTER:

1. Why does the graph start at 10 and end with 25+?

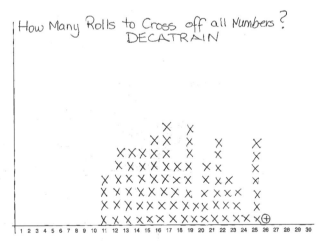

3. How did your games compare with the class findings? Explain.

35

Deca Train

My Prediction 25
What actually happened 23
The difference 2

Erin
gr 2

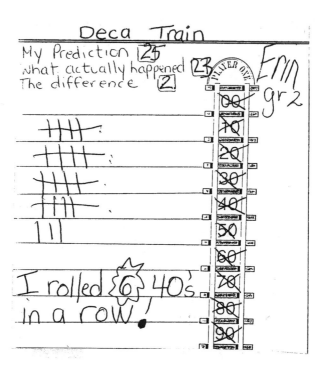

I rolled 6 40's in a row!

Deca Train

My Prediction 39
What actually happened 27
The difference 12

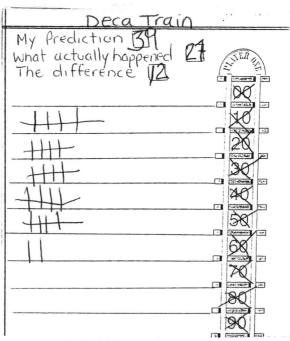

DECA TRAIN CHALLENGER

LEVEL: Grade 1 - 3

SKILLS: Building tens and ones (adding), rounding, probability

PLAYERS: 2 - 4

EQUIPMENT: One decadie and one ten-sided (0-9) die per player, gameboard (see reproducibles), pencil

GETTING STARTED: Each player has their own gameboard.

Player One begins by rolling one decadie and one ten-sided die and adds these two numbers together. Player One now rounds this sum to the nearest ten (decade) and crosses it off their gameboard (e.g. rolls 40 + 8 = 48). Player One now verbalizes "48 is rounded off to 50" and crosses 50 off their gameboard.

Players alternate rolling and crossing off the rounded sum of their two dice. If a number rolled has already been crossed off (i.e. eliminated), then that player misses their turn. The first player to cross off all their numbers is the winner.

VARIATION I: **"Choose" Rules:**

Players roll one decadie and one ten-sided die and add these two numbers together. They determine which two decades their sum falls between (e.g. if a player rolls 50 + 6 = 56, they could choose 50 or 60 and cross one of those numbers off their gameboard). If both of those numbers were already eliminated, then that player misses their turn.

VARIATION II: **Solitaire Version:**

If players prefer to play solo they could add three "X's" underneath their gameboard and circle one "X" every time they can't remove a number. After three "X's" (strikes) have been circled the game ends and you're OUT!

37

THOUGHT PROVOKERS:

1. In Variation I, players make choices throughout the play of the game. According to probability, are certain numbers better to remove than others? Why or why not?

2. Do a comparison of the number of rolls it takes to cross off all your decade numbers in rules as set to Variation I. Explain your findings.

DECA TRAIN CHALLENGER

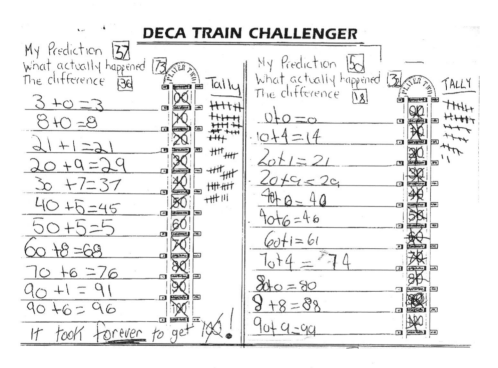

My Prediction 37
What actually happened 73
The difference 36

3 + 0 = 3
8 + 0 = 8
21 + 1 = 21
20 + 9 = 29
30 + 7 = 37
40 + 5 = 45
50 + 5 = 5
60 + 8 = 68
70 + 6 = 76
90 + 1 = 91
90 + 6 = 96
It took forever to get 100!

My Prediction 50
What actually happened 32
The difference 18

0 + 0 = 0
10 + 4 = 14
20 + 1 = 21
20 + 9 = 29
40 + 0 = 40
40 + 6 = 46
60 + 1 = 61
70 + 4 = 74
80 + 0 = 80
8 + 8 = 88
90 + 9 = 99

* sisters gr. 3 and 5 (a friendly family competition!)

DECADICE LINE UP

LEVEL: Kindergarten - Grade 3

SKILLS: Ordering Tens (10's)

PLAYERS: 2 of equal skill level

EQUIPMENT: Four decadice, paper, pencil, one decade number line per player (see reproducibles)

GETTING STARTED: Players roll all four dice. The goal of the game is to be the first player to write the numbers in order and then call out "line up"!

TEACHING NOTE: Have students write the numbers only when ready. Have Kindergarten students match and place the dice directly on the number line. Players can earn a point for correctly verbalizing the sequence.

EXAMPLE: Players Roll:

Player One calls out "line up" and verbalizes what they have recorded:

(10) "ten"; (40) "forty"; (50) "fifty"; (70) "seventy".

If the player is correct, they earn 1 point. In the event that duplicate numbers are rolled, players record both of those numbers.

e.g. player rolls 80, 80, 50, 30 and would then line them up as follows: 30, 50, 80, 80.

Play continues for a set period of time. The player with the most points is the winner.

VARIATION: Have players line up the four numbers from greatest to least.

e.g. 70, 50, 40, 10

THOUGHT PROVOKERS:

1. How often did you roll doubles?

2. How often did you roll triples?

3. How often did you roll a pattern in your sequence of numbers (e.g. 10, 20, 30 or 20, 40, 60)?

4. Do you think four of a kind could ever be rolled?
   How likely is this to happen?

DECAGRAPHIC

LEVEL: Kindergarten - Grade 3

SKILLS: Recognizing and naming decades, graphing, interpreting a bar graph

PLAYERS: Solitaire

EQUIPMENT: One decadie, gameboard (see reproducibles), pencil

GETTING STARTED: Each player has their own gameboard. The goal is to fill in a column (ten up) in as few rolls as possible.

The player rolls the die, verbalizes the number and records it in the appropriate column. The player continues to roll and record numbers until one column is filled in, ten up.

The player then counts up the total number of rolls it took them to complete their "Decagraphic" game. The player records this total on the class graph. The player then colours in their "winning number".

THOUGHT PROVOKERS:

Have students compare their graphs with one another. Some questions to ask about the individual and class graphs might include:

1. Is there one number that always wins or is there a variety of winning numbers?

2. Describe the shape of your graph. Was it an "even" race (neck and neck between numbers) or did one number lead significantly?

3. About how many rolls are needed to "roll out" decagraphic? Compare the class graph with your results. Did you take more or less rolls to play out your game?

Decagraphic

Mady gr 3

00	10	20	30	40	50	60	70	80	90	Total Number of Rolls
				40						
	10			40						
	10			40						
	10	20		40	50	60		80		
	10	20		40	50	60		80	90	75
	10	20	30	40	50	60	70	80	90	
	10	20	30	40	50	60	70	80	90	
	10	20	30	40	50	60	70	80	90	
00	10	20	30	40	50	60	70	80	90	
00	10	20	30	40	50	60	70	80	90	
00	10	20	30	40	50	60	70	80	90	
00	**10**	**20**	**30**	**40**	**50**	**60**	**70**	**80**	**90**	

It took me 75 Rolls to complete this game. I thot it would tacke me less Rolls And I Rolled 40 the most

DECAGRAPHIC II

LEVEL: Grade 2 - 4

SKILLS: Adding tens and ones, rounding to the nearest ten, interpreting bar graphs

PLAYERS: Solitaire

EQUIPMENT: One decadie, cards King - 9 (King = 0, Ace = 1), gameboard (see reproducibles), pencil

GETTING STARTED: Each player has their own gameboard. The goal is to fill in a column (ten up) in as few rolls as possible.

The player turns over one card from their deck and adds it to the number they roll on their decadie.

EXAMPLE: Player One: 20 + 3♥ = 23

Player One rounds to the nearest ten and records 20 + 3 in the 20 column.

The player continues to flip a card and roll, adding, rounding and recording until one column is filled in ten up.

Players then count up the total number of rolls/flips it took them to complete their "Decagraphic II" game. Players record this total on the class graph.

THOUGHT PROVOKERS:

Have students compare their graphs with one another. Some questions to ask about the individual and class graphs might include:

1. Is there one number that always wins or is there a variety of winning numbers?

2. Describe the shape of your graph.

3. On average, how many rolls are needed to "roll out" Decagraphic II? Compare the class graph with your results. Was there a significant difference between your total number of rolls and the class average? Explain your answer.

4. Compare your graphs with graphs from Decagraphic on page 41. Are there any similarities or differences? Explain.

ROLLING A "ROUND"

LEVEL: Grade 3 - 6

SKILLS: Adding tens and ones, rounding to the nearest ten, data analysis, probability

PLAYERS: Solitaire or pairs (competitive or cooperative)

EQUIPMENT: One decadie, one ten-sided (0-9) die, one gameboard (see reproducibles), pencil, highlighter

TEACHING NOTE: This activity originated as a competitive game whereby the winner was determined by whoever had the fewest amount of rolls. Teachers may still choose to play it as it is written below. HOWEVER, as we worked through the Thought Provokers, and played with students the game evolved into a cooperative activity. Students were extremely motivated to predict, analyze data, and draw conclusions from their play. There really was no competitive focus to the game. Students played until one column was filled ten up and then the Thought Provokers were answered. Should you wish to play in this manner, see Thought Provokers, Teaching Tips and samples.

GETTING STARTED: Each player or pair has their own gameboard. The goal of the game is to fill in a column (ten up) in as few rolls as possible.

Player rolls the dice and adds them for a sum, rounds the sum to the nearest ten and records this math sentence in the appropriate column. Players continue to roll until one column is filled in (ten up). Players count up and record the number of rolls to finish the game. The player with the least number of rolls is the winner.

Have students play cooperatively with the Thought Provokers on the next page.

Before the rolling begins, have students predict and record which column will be filled in first (e.g. indicate with a ☺). It is important for students to understand that a prediction is an educated guess that will help them with subsequent predictions. It is neither right nor wrong. Therefore, emphasize fair, random, rolling to generate a true sample.

**TEACHING TIP:** Have students work with the pattern that all plus (+) 0, 1, 2, 3, 4 would be numbers rounded down and all plus (+) 5, 6, 7, 8, 9 would be numbers rounded up.

THOUGHT PROVOKERS:

1. What was the number you predicted? Was there any reason why you chose this number? Explain.

AFTER COMPLETING YOUR GAME:

2. a. Total the number of rolls it took to complete the game.

   b. Go back through and highlight the numbers that were rounded up. How many of your total rolls were rounded up, rounded down?

   c. Was there a significant difference between these two totals?

3. What are the possible outcomes for rounding up and rounding down on your 0-9 die? Are there more for up, down, or are they equally the same? Explain.

4. Create a class graph. About how many rolls to complete a game? What percentage of rolls are rounded up, rounded down?

NOTE: This graph does not show the colour highlighting. Make sure students do this step, as it helps them when analyzing their data.

Rolling A "Round"

Total # of Rolls: 57

Total Round Up: 28

Total Round Down: 29

45

NOTES ON CLASS GRAPH:

1. Students were placed in groups according to how many total rolls to complete.

2. Each group combined their data for total rolls, rounded up/rounded down.

3. It was then placed on a class chart.

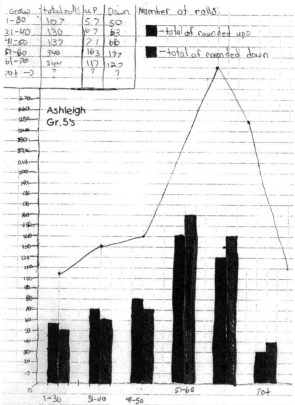

Group	total rolls	uP	Down	Number of rolls
1-30	107	57	50	■ -total of rounded ups
31-40	130	67	63	■ -total of rounded down
41-50	132	21	66	
51-60	340	163	177	
61-70	244	117	122	
70+ -?	?	?	?	

Ashleigh
Gr. 5's

Rolling A Round

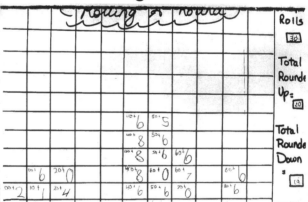

Notice how the student has written the "ones" number larger than the decadie roll. Their explanation - "It helps me focus on the number I need to look at for my rounding rules."

46

DETECTIVE LINE UP

LEVEL:	Grade 3 - 6
SKILLS:	Ordering numbers, identifying and analyzing patterns
PLAYERS:	2
EQUIPMENT:	Four decadice, gameboard (see reproducibles), pencil
GETTING STARTED:	The goal of the game is for players to analyze their rolls for doubles, triples, patterns and sequences of three or four numbers.

Player One rolls all four decadice and looks for any of the following scoring categories:

Any Doubles = 5 points
Two sets of doubles = 25 points
Any Triples = 15 points
Any sequence or pattern of three numbers = 20 points
Any sequence or pattern of four numbers = 50 points

Player records their numbers, what was detected and points earned. Whenever a pattern is rolled, players must record the pattern and the rule (see example).

Detective Line Up

5pts doubles
15pts triples
15pts seq./patt. (3)
50pts seq./patt.(4)

My Numbers...	I detected...	My Score...
20 00 30 40 50 0	30 40 50	15
1 20 30 50 80	20 50 30 (+30)	15
2 00 30 40 70	nothing	
3 30 40 50 60	sequence of 4	50
4 30 50 50 60	doubles	5
5 10 50 70 90	50 70 90 (+20)	15
6 10 20 30 60	10 20 30 sequence	15
7 00 20 60 70	00 20 60 +10 then double it	15
8 30 40 40 70	doubles	5
9 30 50 70 90	30 50 70 90 (+20)	50
10 40 50 60 90	40 50 60	15
11 00 20 80 90	nothing	0
12 00 20 50 40	nothing	0
13 10 10 30 70	10,30,70 double left add 10 doubles	15 15
14 10 30 40 90	nothing	0
15 00 10 30 20	00 10 30 (+10+20)	15
16 30 30 40 40	2 sets of doubles	10
17 40 60 60 70	doubles	5
18 40 50 50 60	40 50 60 double s	20
19 40 60 70 90	40 70 90 40 70 90(+30)	

47

Player Two now rolls all four decadice and looks for their scoring categories.

Players continue to alternate turns. After a set number of rounds the player with the most points is the winner.

Some Scoring Examples:

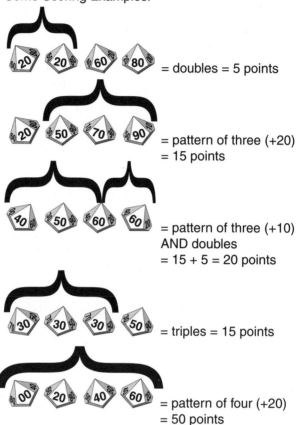

= doubles = 5 points

= pattern of three (+20)
= 15 points

= pattern of three (+10)
AND doubles
= 15 + 5 = 20 points

= triples = 15 points

= pattern of four (+20)
= 50 points

THOUGHT PROVOKERS:

1. What types of patterns were identified and counted for scoring?

2. Were some patterns more frequently rolled than others?

3. How often were doubles/triples rolled?

4. Do you feel the scoring system is fair based on the probability of each event occurring?

5. If this scoring system needs revising, how would you set it up to be fair?

Patterns—
Sequence
of three— 15 pts
of four— 50 pts

Doubles— 5 pts
Triples— 15 pts
4 of a kind— 50
cho?rea 3
5-3
Nov 21st

Detective Line Up

Thought Provokers:

1. What types of patterns were identifi
and counted for scoring? There was
+20, +30, +10 +20, +10 double it, double it +10 as
the patterns

2. Were some patterns more frequently rolle
than others? Yes the most frequently rolled was
+20.

3. How often were doubles/triples rolled?
We rolled doubles occasionaly and didn't
roll tripples.

4 Do you feel the scoring system is fair
based on the probability of each event
happening? no 4 in a row is too comon I think it
should score 30 points, I think two sets
of pairs should score 25 points.

TWEENIES

LEVEL: Grade 1 - 3 (Variation: Grade 4 - 6)

SKILLS: Comparing numbers 0 - 90
Variation: comparing numbers 0 - 9 090

PLAYERS: 3

EQUIPMENT: One decadie per player, bingo chips or other counters, decade number line (see reproducibles)

GETTING STARTED: Each player rolls one die and says their number out loud. Players compare their numbers. The "Between" or "Tweenie" number wins the round and takes a counter. It may be helpful for players to have a number line.

EXAMPLE:

Player One	Player Two	Player Three

Players verbalize as follows:

Player Two says "80 is the greatest". Player Three says "20 is the least". Player One says "60 is between 80 and 20" and earns 1 point.

Play continues for a set period of time. The player with the most points wins.

VARIATION I:

Grade 4 - 6:

All players alternate rolling two dice, creating numbers between 0 and 9 090. Have players roll their number on a chart as follows:

Thousands/Hundreds	Tens/Ones

60 ... 20

= 6 020

"six thousand twenty"

EXAMPLE:

Player One	Player Two	Player Three

Nine thousand ten is the greatest, two thousand eighty is the least and eight thousand twenty is between. Player One earns 1 point.

This game provides excellent practice for both reading and comparing larger numbers.

VARIATION II: Have players roll their dice secretly. Players may choose to arrange their dice and set them once done. All players reveal their numbers. The between number wins.

THOUGHT PROVOKERS:

Grade 1 - 3:

After a set period of time should players have about the same amount of points? Explain. Compare your answer to your game.

Grade 4 - 6:

1. Record all the rolls during play. What were your lowest and highest recorded "Tweenie" wins? What was the average "Tweenie" win?

2. Did the players in your group earn an even number of points? How many rounds do you think you need to play to "even" it out?

3. Graph the distribution of the rolls. What type of graph could be used to best display the data? For Grade 4 - 6 playing with two decadice the largest possible number you can roll is 9 090. The smallest number is 0. We suggest increments of 500.

"Tweenies"   Tweenies

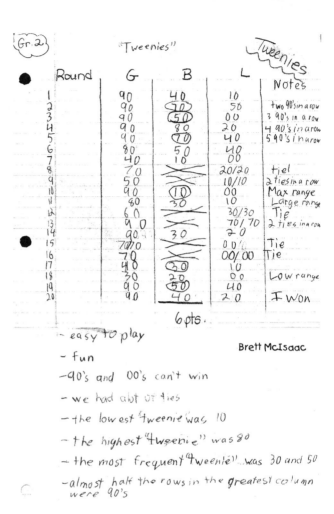

Round	G	B	L	Notes
1	90	40	10	
2	90	(70)	50	two 90's in a row
3	90	(50)	00	3 90's in a row
4	90	80	20	4 90's in a row
5	90	(70)	40	5 90's in a row
6	80	50	40	
7	40	10	00	
8	70	X	20/20	tie!
9	50	X	10/10	2 ties in a row
10	90	(10)	00	Max range
11	80	30	10	Large range
12	60	X	30/30	Tie
13	90	X	70/70	2 ties in a row
14	90	30	20	
15	70/70	X	00/0	Tie
16	70	X	00/00	Tie
17	40	(30)	10	
18	30	20	00	Low range
19	90	(50)	40	
20	90	40	20	I won

6 pts.

Brett McIsaac

- easy to play
- fun
- 90's and 00's can't win
- we had alot of ties
- the lowest "tweenie" was 10
- the highest "tweenie" was 80
- the most frequent "tweenie" was 30 and 50
- almost half the rows in the greatest column were 90's

Tweenies

least tweenies!

Jason Stewart 4N

Record all players rolls.

Round	G	B		L	
1	9010	8020		3010	
2	9020	6000		1050	
3	3010	(1040)		0030	
4	7010	6040		1050	
5	8060	6050	5070	3030	
6 *me*	9040	7060	2080	0000	
7 ☆	7020	8040		5070	5070
8	8040	6090	(4030)	0080	
9	8090	4010	4030	3020	
10	6090	(6030)	2040	0060	
11	8040 8040	5010		2040	
13	8080	4000	(1000)	0020	
14					
15	8070	6040	5070	4060	
16	4060	3070	2010	0060	
17	9090	8000	7090	5090	

NOTE:

The group added another player and had a group of 4.

Graph the Distribution of Your Rolls

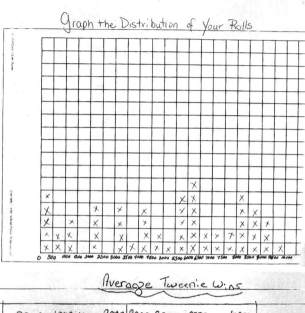

0   500 1000 1500 2000 2500 3000 3500 4000 4500 5000 5500 6000 6500 7000 7500 8000 8500 9000 9500 10000

Average Tweenie Wins

0000-1000	1000-2000	2000-3000	3000 - 4000
0	0	1	3

4000-5000	5000-6000	6000-7000	7000-8000
10	2	2	0

1.4858   2.3377   3.5117   4.4066   5.4900   6.5690
7.4273   8.4625   9.3715   10.4520   11.2290
12.4707 13.4785   14.4707   15.3727   16.631
17.6565   18.-848

Average Tweenie Wins

TWEENIES VARIATION:

	Col 1	Col 2	Col 3
1	7090	1060	1010
2	7070	(1030)	1010
3	7020	3020	(5060)
4	6090	6010	0200
5	7020	8000	5050
6	4090		6000
7	9050	2060	0080
8	4090	3040	1030
9	5030	3010	1050
10	4030		1060
11	6020	(4060)	0000
12	9050	4040	0080
13	6050	3010	3040
14	9030	9020	4060
15	5090	5020	1070
16	5070	(3000)	(3000)
17	8000	7010	1020
18	1090	(1050)	1050
19	(5060)	4020	4090
20	7000	5010	

(2 3 4 5 6 7 8 9 10)

(CASSIE) 8 r 5 odder

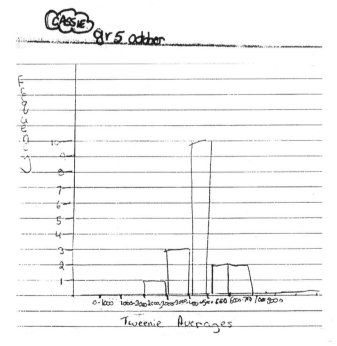

Frequency

Tweenie Averages

0-1000 1000-2000 2000-3000 3000-4000 4000-5000 550 600-700 100-800

Tweenie Thought Provokers

A) ① The lowest "tweenie" number that won was:

1050

B) ② My "tweenie" wins are:

$$
\begin{array}{r}
1050 \\
+\ 4060 \\
+\ 3000 \\
+\ 1050 \\
\hline
9160
\end{array}
$$

C) ③ My average "tweenie" win was:

$9160 \div 4 = 2290$

① add up the numbers
② Take that number and divide it by
how many numbers you add

The "Average" of all the "Averages"

1) Add up all 18 numbers

2) Divide that total by 18

$\underset{4619}{}$

4619   x x x x x x x x x x x x x

CHIP TAC TOE

LEVEL: Grade 1 - 3

SKILLS: Learning numbers on the Hundred Board

PLAYERS: 2 or 4

EQUIPMENT: Two decadice, bingo chips, hundred board (see reproducibles)

GETTING STARTED: The goal of the game is to be the first player to get five bingo chips of their own colour in a row vertically, horizontally or diagonally. Players share one game-board and choose their own colour of bingo chips. Player One rolls the two dice and places a chip on any number that falls between the two numbers rolled. The player may also choose to place their chip on the actual number rolled (e.g. a player rolls 20 and 70 and may choose any number between 20 and 70 including 20 and 70). Players alternate rolling the dice and placing chips on the board. Each turn players verbalize (e.g. "60, 80, I'm placing my chip on sixty eight which is between 60 and 80."). A player may not put their chip on a space occupied by their opponent. If a player rolls a double on their turn (e.g. 60, 60), they may remove any chip of their opponent's. This leaves this space open and available to either player on a future turn.

If a player gets five in a row, they verbalize "Chip Tac Toe", read their numbers to their opponent and win that round. Play continues for a set period of time. The player who has won the most rounds is the winner.

THOUGHT PROVOKERS:

1. On average, how many rolls will it take before one player succeeds in getting five chips in a row? How could you keep track?

2. How frequently do you think doubles will be rolled during the play of the game? Keep track and compare this result to your prediction.

TEN FOR ME

LEVEL: Grade 2 - 4

SKILLS: Adding, patterning, place value, learning numbers on a hundred board

PLAYERS: 2

EQUIPMENT: One decadie, one ten-sided (0-9) die per player, blank hundred board (see reproducibles), pencil

GETTING STARTED: Each player needs their own gameboard. The goal of the game is to be the first player to fill in ten spaces on their gameboard in any direction (horizontally, vertically, or diagonally). However, this does not include filling in the top row (1-10) only, or the last column (10-100); as these could be quickly filled in by rolling the decadie or the ten-sided (0-9) die by itself.

To begin, Player One rolls the decadie and ten-sided die together and adds these to find their sum; or, Player One can choose to just roll one die by itself and record this number on their gameboard.

EXAMPLE: Player One rolls:

Player One fills in 36 in the appropriate space on their board.

Player Two rolls only one die: 5

Player Two fills in 5 in the fifth space in the top row of their gameboard.

If a player rolls and the corresponding space has already been filled in, that player misses their turn.

Players alternate rolling and filling in their own gameboards until one player has successfully filled in ten consecutive spaces in any direction. This player then verbalizes "Ten for Me" and wins the game.

TEACHING TIPS: 1. How do you fill in the hundred (100) space on your board (players do not add their dice)? Players can roll the following to <u>partially</u> fill in their hundred (100) space:

58

a) Roll

Player can record 00 in the one hundred space and then attempt to roll a 1 on their ten-sided die (0-9) on a future turn.

b) Roll

Player can record 0 in the one hundred space and then attempt to roll a 10 on their decadie on a future turn.

c) Roll

Player can record 00 in the one hundred space and then attempt to roll a 1 on their ten-sided die on a future turn.

Players can roll the following in one turn to <u>completely</u> fill in their one hundred space:

a) Roll

Player can record 100 in the one hundred space and this is now completely filled in.

2. Have students alternate rolling one die; either the ten-sided (0-9) or decadie by itself. This helps to fill in the top row of numbers (1-10) and the decade numbers (10-100) down the far right column. These numbers are like "benchmarks" that guide the students to locate where other numbers belong (e.g. if a player rolls and the 2 is filled in on the top row, they know that 82 will be found below in the second column).

Similarly, if 80 has already been filled in on the far right column then to locate 82, it is only two spaces ahead (in the next row that contains the numbers from eighty one to ninety).

What did this game teach?

It helps with multiplication. Because of the groups you can jump to a number. This game makes you look for patterns. It helps with subtracting too. And counting back to find the right space, to put the number in. This game was fun. You had to concintrat. I'm going to teach my friends.

Ten for me

BLANK HUNDRED BOARD Madison Gr. 3

1	2	3	4	5	6	7	8	9	10
11	12	13	14	15	16		18		20
21		23	24			27	28	29	30
	32		34				38		40
41	42	43	44	45	46	47	48	49	50
51		53	54					59	60
	62			66	67				
	72		74	75		77		79	
			84						90
			94			97		99	100

I Won against my sister

TREASURE HUNT

LEVEL:	Grade 1 - 3 (Variation: Grade 4 - 6)
SKILLS:	Logical reasoning, odd/even, less than / greater than Variation: factors, multiples
PLAYERS:	2
EQUIPMENT:	One decadie, one ten-sided (0-9) die, hundred board (see reproducibles), bingo chips
GETTING STARTED:	The goal of the game is to identify the hidden roll in as few guesses as possible. Player One secretly rolls the decadie and ten-sided die creating a two-digit number. Player Two now begins to ask a series of math questions to identify the hidden number. Each question counts as 1 point against that player. Lowest number of guesses wins.
TEACHING TIP:	For younger grades we suggest that a hundred board be used as a visual record of the guesses. As a player makes their guesses, they cover up the corresponding number(s) with their bingo chips. Players can then narrow down the secret number in a more organized, visual manner.
EXAMPLE:	**Player One's secret roll:** 60 4 6 = 64

Player Two's Question	Player One's Response
Is it Odd?	No
Is it less than 50?	No
Is it between 70 and 80?	No
Is it less than 70?	Yes
Is it greater than 60?	Yes
Is it 62?	No
Is it 64?	Yes

It took seven questions to guess the correct number, so Player One now has 7 points for the round. Players alternate turns for a set number of rounds. The player with the LEAST points against them wins.

VARIATION: For Grades 4 to 6, ask questions that involve factoring/multiples (e.g. Is the number divisible by 3?).

THOUGHT PROVOKERS:

1. If you were to give advice to a new player, what type of questions would you tell them to begin with and why?

2. What type of questions helped eliminate or narrow down possible numbers?

3. Are some math questions better to ask than others?

Treasure Hunt gr. 5

① I between 30-70? No

② I between 00-40? Yes

③ Is one of tens digits even? No

④ I between 20-40? Yes   30-10

⑤ Is the ten digit greater than 60? NO

---

① Are one of the numbers even? NO

② Are both numbers smaller than 50? NO

③ Are both numbers smaller than 70? Yes   50-30

IN THE ZONE

LEVEL: Snap: Grade 2 - 5
                        Non-Snap: Grade 1 - 3
                        Variation: money

SKILLS: Comparing numbers 0 - 90, reading numbers

PLAYERS: 2 of equal skill level, sitting side by side

EQUIPMENT: Two decadice, cards King - 9 (King = 0, Ace = 1)

GETTING STARTED: Players sit side by side so that they are building and reading the two-digit numbers properly. To begin, players divide the deck in half and place each half face down in front of themselves. Two decadice are rolled to create at least a ten number range (e.g. 40-80 range is established for the round). Now players turn over the top card from each of their decks to cooperatively make a two-digit number. One player turning over the "tens" digit and the other player turning over the "ones". The goal is to build a number that will fit in the range and to be the first player to verbalize it. Numbers ending in 0 are allowed.

EXAMPLE: **Two decadice rolled:**

Range is 40 to 80

1.   **Player One**   **Player Two**
               (tens)   (ones)

Twenty four does not fit in the range of 40 to 80 so players both flip a new card and place it on top of their previous card.

2.   **Player One**   **Player Two**
               (tens)   (ones)

Thirty eight does not fit. Players flip new cards.

3.

Player One
(tens)

Player Two
(ones)

Fifty six does fit in the range. The first player to verbalize "fifty six fits" takes all of the cards.

A new range is rolled and a new round begins. Play for a set period of time. The player with the most cards is the winner.

 **TEACHING TIP:**

It may work more smoothly for one player to flip both cards and one player to roll the dice. Let players decide!

VARIATION I:

**PLAY IN THE SLOW ZONE -
A NON-SNAP VARIATION:**

Players roll the two decadice to create at least a ten number range. Each player turns over their own two cards, the first being the tens number and the second being the ones number. Players now check to see if their two-digit number fits into the "ZONE". If so, they earn their opponents cards and place them with their own into a point pile. If both players fit in the ZONE, players keep their own cards and place them into their point pile.

EXAMPLE:

ROUND 1:

Two decadice rolled:

Range is 10 to 50

Player One's Cards

Player Two's Cards

Player Two verbalizes "41 fits between 10 and 50", 69 does not and takes Player One's cards.

ROUND 2:

Two decadice rolled:

Range is 40 to 90

Player One's Cards   **Player Two's Cards**

Both players verbalize their numbers and keep their own cards.

TEACHING TIP: Have players sit side-by-side to read numbers properly (from left to right).

VARIATION II: Play "In The Slow Zone" as a money game, by adding the following:

After players flip over their cards and build their numbers, they now "build" this number using dimes and pennies (on a place-value chart/board).

Play out the round as in the previous rules, but players take the coins instead of the cards. The player with the most money wins.

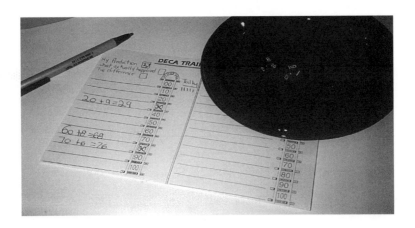

65

DECK YA

LEVEL:	Grade 1 - 3
SKILLS:	Comparing numbers 0 - 90
PLAYERS:	2 - 3 of equal skill level
EQUIPMENT:	Two decadice, cards King - 9, (King = 0, Ace = 1)
GETTING STARTED:	Each player is dealt seven cards. The rest of the cards are placed face down in the center. To start the round, the two decadice are rolled to set the range. The goal of the game is to be the first player to get rid of all the cards in their hand by building two-digit numbers that fit in the range. At the same time, players draw one card from the pile and add this new number to their hand. Each player now begins to build their numbers using each card only once.

EXAMPLE:

Two decadice rolled:

Range is 10 to 50

Player One's Cards

Player Two's Cards

Player One verbalizes and places down the following numbers:

29, 18, 26, 41 and says "Decked Ya!"

Player Two verbalizes and places down the following numbers:

29, 36, 40 and is left with 7 and 0.

In this example, Player One wins the round and earns all the cards.

Players may lay down a number that fits right on the range. If neither player gets rid of all their cards on the first round (usually the case), play continues keeping the same range. Players now draw one or two new cards, always keeping an even number of cards to play from.

TEACHING TIP: There is a lot of strategy in selecting and building numbers to fit in the range. In the last example, could Player Two have gone out by making any different numbers?

Encourage students to analyze various number combinations before making their final moves.

VARIATION I: Play a non-speed variation where it is no longer the first player to place down their cards to win. Both players could then win in the same round, taking all of their own cards and placing them into their point pile.

VARIATION II: Play "Deck Ya" with similar rules with the exception of rolling four decadice; building two numbers into the thousands place and creating a range. Players re-roll all four dice if the range is a thousand or less. Players will need to begin with eleven cards in their hand and can build two to four-digit numbers with their cards. At the same time, players draw one card from the pile and add this new number to their hand. Players now begin to build their numbers, in an attempt to be the first player to lay down all of their cards.

EXAMPLE: Four decadice rolled:

Range is 3 080 to 6 090

Player One's Cards Only:

Possible numbers built that would fit:

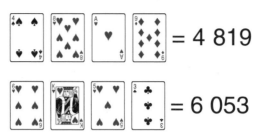 = 4 819

= 6 053

= 5 972

68

PONDERING PREDICTIONS

LEVEL: Grade 1 - 3

SKILLS: Comparing numbers 0 - 90, greater than / less than, odd / even

PLAYERS: 2 - 4

EQUIPMENT: One decadie per player, one regular die, paper, pencil

GETTING STARTED: Each player rolls their die three times and chooses the best "least" or best "greatest" number. These numbers are recorded and players circle the number they have selected for the round. To determine which player earns the point for that round, the regular die is then rolled:

Roll 1, 2, or 3, the "best least" earns a point.

Roll 4, 5, or 6, the "best greatest" earns a point.

EXAMPLE:

	Roll #1	Roll #2	Roll #3
Player One:	50	10	(90)

Player One selects 90 as their best "greatest" number.

	Roll #1	Roll #2	Roll #3
Player Two:	(20)	60	40

Player Two selects 20 as their best "least" number.

Player Three:	30	70	80

In the previous three-player example, Player Three already knows they cannot earn a point.

The regular die is rolled (roll = 4: greatest number wins) and Player One earns 1 point as the "Best Greatest".

Play continues for a set period of time. The player with the most points is the winner. In the event of a tie (i.e. both players choose the same number) both players earn a point.

TEACHING TIP: We found it best for players to roll their die hidden from their opponent. We have them sit side by side with a binder or other divider between them. Players take their rolls, record, and make their selections secretly before determining who earns a point.

VARIATION: Have players attempt to roll the "best between" number after three rolls. Regular die roll: 1-2 least winner, 3-4 between winner, 5-6 greatest winner.

RANGE GAME

LEVEL: Grade 2 - 3, Grade 4 - 7

SKILLS: Grade 2 - 3: Comparing numbers 0 - 90, "betweeness", probability

Grade 4 - 7: Recording/analyzing data, graphing, percent, probability

PLAYERS: 2

EQUIPMENT: Two decadice, paper, pencil, gameboard (see reproducibles), highlighters

GETTING STARTED: **Step One:** Setting the Range

Each player rolls their die. These two numbers establish the target range (e.g. rolls 60 - 90) for the round. The range for this round would be 30, because the difference between ninety and sixty is thirty.

NOTE: If doubles are rolled, have players record as in example (round 7). No points are earned when the range is 0. Players proceed to the next round.

Both players now attempt to roll a number that falls between the target range.

Step Two: Scoring (see example on next page)

O = 1 point $\circledcirc$ = 2 points. (bullseye)

Players record the set target range and then take their own die. Each player now rolls their own die. If a player's roll falls between the established target range, they earn a point. Both players can earn a point each round.

If a player rolls one of the numbers of the established range, they earn a bullseye worth 2 points.

TEACHING TIP: Run this gameboard off on white paper!

EXAMPLE:

Round	Target Rolls	Range	Player One	Player Two
1	80/60	20	00	50
2	50/00	50	(30)	70
3	30/10	20	((30))	60
4	60/50	10	90	00
5	80/20	60	(30)	(60)
6	60/50	10	((50))	((50))
7	80/80	0	—	—
8	50/30	20	(40)	60
9	70/10	60	(40)	(30)

After 9 Rounds: 8 pts. 4 pts.

This scoring system is very easy for players to use. At the end of a set number of rounds (e.g. 50 rounds) players simply count up the number of circles in their column. After 9 rounds, Player One has earned 8 points and Player Two has earned 4 points.

 **TEACHING TIP:**   Once all the rounds are finished, players can analyze and interpret their data. See Thought Provokers.

THOUGHT PROVOKERS:

To explore the probability, have the players record for each round, the rolls, range and how often they earn a point or bonus point, as in the example (see reproducible for gameboard).

1. How often does a range of 0 happen?

2. How often did you earn a point?

3. How often did both players earn a point?

4. How great of a range is needed to probably earn a point? Explain your answer.

5. Are there any rolls that guarantee players a point?

6. Can you design a question for other players to answer about their data?

7. What is the best type of graph(s) to use when displaying your data?

Jenn Schofield
gr 6

Range Game Questions

Range Game Results   Oct. 26

Legend: Jill + Kyla, Jen + Laurel, Robb + Cam

good choice

Each group had totally different results.

1. How many rounds did you complete?
   My group completed all 20 rounds. ✓ ①

2. How often did the range of 0 happen?
   The range of 0 happened 2 times. ①

3. How often did both players score one point?
   Both players scored one point 3 times. ①

4. How often did both players score a bullseye?
   Both players scored a bullseye 2 times. ①

5. Are there any rolls that guarantee players points?
   Yes, there are rolls that guarantee point, when
   you roll a 00 and a 90. ②

6. Design a question for other players to answer about
   their data.

72

RANGE GAME GAMEBOARD

.00 10 20 30 40 50 60 70 80 90

Round	Target Rolls	Range	Player One	Player Two	Colour Code	
1	70-50	20	40	(60)		Blue
2	60-30	30	(40)	00		Blue
3	80-60	20	(70)	(80)		Purple
4	00-00	50	90	(10)		blue yellow
5	50-20	30	60	00		Green
6	20-00	20	40	(00)		purple
7	90-00	90	(80)	(90)		purple
8	70-00	70	(00)	40		purple
9	60-00	60	(40)	(30)		Red
10	90-10	80	00	(40)		blue
11	50-00	50	(40)	60		blue
12	50-00	50	60	(10)		blue
13	60-30	30	(60)	(30)		Orange
14	70-30	40	(30)	(70)		orange
15	60-10	50	(40)	90		blue
16	90-30	60	(50)	(80)		Red
17	90-90	00	00	70		yellow
18	40-00	40	70	(30)		blue
19	90-50	40	(70)	(70)		Red
20	80-40	40	(40)	30		Green

PLAYER ONE'S TOTAL 16

PLAYER TWO'S TOTAL 18

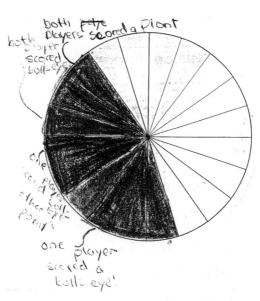

both players scored a piont
both players scored bull-eye
one player scored other bull point
one player scored a bull-eye!

Laura
Manea
gr6

KATIE + GEORGIA
Both had two red
They have three blue
We have no blue
We have eleven yellow
They have eight yellow
They have two orange
We have one orange
They have five green
we have four green

73

Range Game

Name: Madiso.
gr 2

Thought Provokers:

1. How often did a range of O happen?
   It hapind 4 times out of 20

2. How often did you score one point?
   it hapind 4 times out of 20

3. a) How often did both players score a point? 3 time's out
   b) a double point? of 20,

4. How great of a range is needed to probably score a point?
   50 point

5. Are there any rolls that guarantee players a point?
   00 out of 90

6. Can you write a question for other players to answer about their data?

74

KEEP THE RANGE OPEN

LEVEL: Grade 3 - 6

SKILLS: Probability, place value, "betweeness"

PLAYERS: 4: 2 vs. 2

EQUIPMENT: Two decadice, cards King - 9 (King = 0, Ace = 1)

GETTING STARTED: **Step One:**

In the first step, teams get to roll the two decadice a maximum of three times. They must choose as they roll, which maximum difference they wish to keep for step two. Teams will want to have the maximum range possible.

EXAMPLE: **Team One, Roll One:**

Team chooses to re-roll as it is a small range (only a difference of ten).

Team One, Roll Two:

Team One chooses to accept this roll and take it into step two.

Teams are allowed a third roll, but if it's not their best range, they are stuck with it for the next step of the game. A double roll (e.g. 20/20 or 40/40) on the last roll means players must play with a 10 point difference. When a 10 point difference is rolled players must use the rolled numbers as one of the numbers in the new range (e.g. the team rolls 20/20 and can choose 10/20 or 20/30).

Step Two:

Once both teams have their established range, all players are dealt six cards each. These will now be used to create two-digit numbers that fall into their own team's range. Players may lay down a number that fits right on the range. Players do not show their cards to their team mate.

Set Up:

Players from the same team sit side-by-side so that the numbers are built and read correctly.

	Roll/Range
Team One (Players One and Two)	20 to 70
Team Two (Players Three and Four)	10 to 40

Play begins with Team One. On every turn, each team member contributes one of their cards to build a two-digit number to fit within their range. They must alternate who starts the number with the 10's value.

EXAMPLE:

Only Team One's moves have been recorded below:

Player One's Cards:

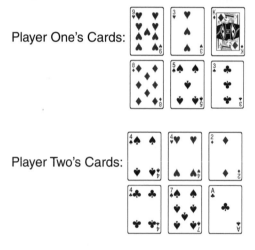

Player Two's Cards:

Team One **Player One** starts and puts down a 3 and says 30. Player Two puts down a 7 to complete 37. Team One takes the two cards and puts them into their point pile for a two-digit number that fits into their range of 20 to 70 (Team Two would then take their turn).

Team One **Player Two** starts and puts down a 4 and says 40. Player One puts down an 8 to complete 48. Team One earns their cards for building a two-digit number that fits into their range (Team Two would then take their turn).

Team One **Player One** starts and puts down a 3 and says 30. Player Two puts down a 4 to complete 34. Team One earns their cards for building a two-digit number that fits into their range (Team Two would then take their turn).

Team One **Player Two** starts and puts down a 4 and says 40. Player One puts down a 5 to complete 45. Team One earns their cards for building a two-digit number that fits into their range (Team Two would then take their turn).

Team One **Player One** starts and puts down a 9 and says 90. Player Two puts down a 1 to complete 91. Ninety one does not fit in the range, therefore Team One earns no cards (Team Two would then take their turn).

Team One **Player Two** starts and puts down a 2 and says 20. Player One puts down a 0 to complete 20. Team One earns their cards for building a two-digit number that fits into their range (Team Two finishes their final turn).

The team with the most cards in their point pile wins the round.

 **TEACHING TIP:** This is a great game for looking at probability in Step One. Have the children discuss strategy for how they choose their range (see Decidedly Different and refer to the Outcome Chart on page 220). This game is also excellent for developing strategies for players to use when building their numbers in place value.

THOUGHT PROVOKERS:

1. What strategy did you use in selecting your 10's and 1's cards as you were building your numbers? Would you play certain numbers early in the round rather than later?

2. Are certain numbers better used as ones or tens?

3. If you rolled a double on your last roll, how did your team choose to set the 10-difference range?

DECADE DUEL

(invented by Andrea Felling, grade 5)

LEVEL: Grade 2 - 5

SKILLS: Place value, comparing numbers 0 - 90, probability

PLAYERS: 2 - 4

EQUIPMENT: Two ten-sided (0-9) dice and two decadice per group, pencil, paper

GETTING STARTED: All players take turns rolling the two ten-sided dice and forming two-digit numbers. Players should roll on a place value board or mat to help establish their number (see Variations for alternate rules). Players now record their two-digit number on paper.

EXAMPLE:

Player One's Roll		Player Two's Roll		Player Three's Roll	
Tens	Ones	Tens	Ones	Tens	Ones
6	8	3	7	7	9

Once all players have rolled their numbers, the two decadice are rolled to set the range.

Roll:

Range is 10 to 60

Players now compare their number to the range. If it fits into the range, they earn a point. In the example above, Player Two earns 1 point because 37 falls between 10 and 60. The other players do not receive any points.

Players re-roll their ten-sided dice and build a new two-digit number. The decadice are re-rolled for a new range. Play continues for a set period of time. The player with the most points is the winner.

* If the decadice are the same (e.g. 20/20) then no players earn a point.

* If a player rolls a number that falls right on the range (e.g. 60) they earn double points.

78

 **TEACHING TIP:** Have players record all rounds so that they can explore the Thought Provokers. Have students circle their points.

THOUGHT PROVOKERS:

1. Approximately how often are doubles rolled on the decadice? Do you agree with the rule that no players earn a point when doubles are rolled?

2. About how often will a two-digit number fall right on the range? Do you agree with the rule that a player earns double points? Explain.

3. How big of a range (difference) is necessary to earn a point?

4. What is the average range rolled?

VARIATION: Players roll their two ten-sided dice and can decide how to form their number. Have them explore how this might help them to maximize their chances for scoring. Or would it?

Decade Duel

Mackenzie
Grade 5

My Number	The Range	Difference	Points
60	30-40	10	0
6	10-40	30	0
84	40-60	20	0
26	0-70	70	✓
31	50-80	30	0
10	20-70	50	0
76	0-20	20	0
44	80-80	0	0
93	70-70	0	0
28	20-30	10	✓
19	30-30	0	0
91	10-20	10	0

Decade Duel   Mel gr 5
Stem Leaf Plot

Distribution of 100 Rolls
Range of Possible Rolls 00 - 99

STEM 10's	LEAVES 1's										
0	1	2	3	4	5	5	7	8	9	9	
1	1	1	2	3	3	4	4	5	9	9	
2	0	0	2	3	4	4	6	6	7	8	8	9
3	0	1	3	3	5	5	6	6	7	7	7
4	2	5	5	6	7	7	9	9			
5	0	0	1	1	3	5	7	7	9		
6	0	1	2	2	2	3	5	8	8	9	
7	1	2	5	5	5	5	6	8	8		
8	0	1	1	1	2	3	5	6	6	7	9	9
9	1	2	2	2	3	4	6	7	8		

NOTE: Over time this distribution is fairly even.

80

EIGHT'S ENOUGH

LEVEL: Grade 3 - 6

SKILLS: Building numbers to 99, comparing numbers, predicting, probability

PLAYERS: 2

EQUIPMENT: Two decadice, cards King - 9 (King = 0, Ace = 1)

GETTING STARTED: Both players are dealt eight cards. The goal of the game is to accumulate the most cards (1 point per card). Players sit across from each other. At the start of each turn a player will draw one card.

Player One draws a card and then selects any two cards from their hand and places down a two-digit number. Player Two then rolls the decadice. If the two-digit number falls into the range of the roll, then Player One may take the two cards and place them into their point pile. If the number does not fit, the cards are replaced into the player's hand.

Player Two now draws a card, selects any two cards from their hand and places down a two-digit number. Player One rolls the decadice. If the two-digit number falls into the range of the roll, then Player Two may take the two cards and place them into their point pile. If the number does not fit, the cards are replaced into the player's hand.

Players continue to alternate turns making two-digit numbers and rolling the range, remembering to draw one new card each turn. The game is over when one player places down their last two cards and this number fits into the rolled range.

Players count up their cards to determine the winner. The player with the most cards wins.

EXAMPLE: Player One makes a two-digit number with their cards.

 = 25

Player Two now rolls the decadice.

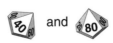 and

81

Since 25 does not fall between 40 and 80, Player One must replace the 2 and 5 cards back into their hand.

BONUS SCORING RULES

1. If a number built fits right on the range (e.g. if the decadice range is 40-80 and the player lays down a 4 and 0) then the player may take an additional two card bonus from the draw pile and place these directly into their point pile.

2. If a number built fits into a 10 difference range (e.g. if the decadice range is 10-20 and the player lays down a 1 and 6) then the player may take an additional one card bonus from the draw pile and place this card into their point pile.

 TEACHING TIP: Have players verbalize the size of the range with each roll.

THOUGHT PROVOKERS:

1. Why do you suppose players earn a bonus point if their number fits into a ten number range?

2. How often do you think players will earn bonus points for having numbers right on the range?

3. Is it less likely to have a number fit into a ten number range than to have a number fit right on the range?

FIGURE EIGHT

LEVEL: Grade 3 - 6

SKILLS: Building and comparing numbers 0 - 88, rounding

PLAYERS: 2

EQUIPMENT: Cards King - 8 (King = 0, Ace = 1), one decadie

GETTING STARTED: Players divide the deck evenly between themselves. Each player takes eight cards, flipping two at a time, building four two-digit numbers.

As players flip their two cards they can analyze the combinations and decide how they wish to set them.

Once these four numbers have been set, they remain that way for the entire game.

EXAMPLE:

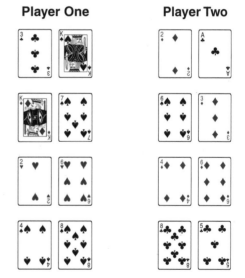

Players now alternate rolling the decadie. All the two-digit numbers that can be rounded off to match the number rolled on the decadie are removed. The die is then re-rolled. The player who removes all of their cards first wins.

EXAMPLE:

Roll One:

Player Two rounds 85 to 90 and removes those cards. Player One has no move.

Roll Two:

Neither player can round to 40.

Roll Three:

Player One rounds 07 to 10 and removes those cards. Player Two has no move.

Roll Four:

Player One rounds 48 to 50 and removes those cards. Player Two rounds 46 to 50 and removes those cards.

Roll Five:

Neither player can round to 40.

Roll Six:

Player One removes 30 and also rounds 26 to 30 and removes those cards. Player One has now removed all their cards and wins the round.

VARIATION:

For Grades 1 - 2:

Have students build their "figure-eight" (i.e. four number combinations). Roll the die. Students do not need to round their number. If the 10's value matches the decade, they may take off their cards (e.g. if 20 is rolled and a player has 26).

THOUGHT PROVOKERS:

1. According to probability, is there any strategy involved when building the two-digit numbers for rounding off?

2. About how many rolls of the decadie do you think it usually takes for one player to remove all their cards? Predict before playing and compare your answers.

FLIPPIN' OUT

LEVEL: Grade 3 - 6

SKILLS: Building and comparing numbers to 99, rounding, probability

PLAYERS: 2 - 4

EQUIPMENT: One decadie, cards King - 9 (King = 0, Ace = 1), gameboard (see reproducibles)

GETTING STARTED: Each player turns over two cards from the deck and chooses how to make their two-digit number.

Players then round their two-digit number to the nearest 10's place.

Players now roll the decadie and generate a target. The player with the rounded number that is closest to the target number earns the cards.

If there is a tie, both players keep their cards.

EXAMPLE:

Player One's Cards   **Player Two's Cards**

Player One rounds their number off and says 40. Player Two rounds their number off and says 60.

Decadie Roll:

Player Two earns the cards, since 60 is closer to 80.

In the event of a tie (i.e. both players are equally close to the number rolled on the decadie) both players earn their cards plus a bonus card.

The next round begins by players building a new number with the remaining cards. A new target is rolled each round.

Play continues for a set period of time. The player with the most cards is the winner.

THOUGHT PROVOKERS:

1. Is there any strategy involved when building a number to round off?

2. Does it make any difference as to whether you make your number before or after the other player(s)? If so, should players take turns?

3. About how often do you suppose you would build a number that matches the target number? Is this very probable?

VARIATION:

Players turn over three cards and make a three-digit number. Players then round their number to the nearest 100's place. Players roll one ten-sided die, then a decadie and generate a target.

  = 830

The player with the rounded number that is closest to the target earns the cards.

 **TEACHING TIP:**

Children have their own colour of bingo chip when playing. After players have built and rounded their number, they place their bingo chip on the corresponding number found on the (0 – 100) number line. Next, the decadie is rolled and placed directly onto its corresponding number on the number line. This provides the perfect visual reference for players to determine whose rounded number is closer to the target number (see diagram).

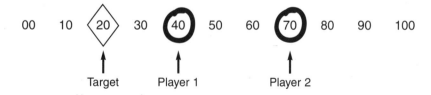

IT'S A TOSS UP

LEVEL: Grade 2 - 4

SKILLS: Place value to 9 090, reading large numbers

PLAYERS: 2

EQUIPMENT: Two decadice per player

GETTING STARTED: Each player rolls their two dice and makes the largest four-digit number possible and verbalizes it to their opponent. The player with the largest number earns 2 points.

EXAMPLE:

Player One   Player Two

six thousand twenty   four thousand thirty

Player One earns 2 points.

In the event of a tie (both players have the same number), a tie breaker must be played. Each player rolls the dice again. The first player to roll a number greater than the tie earns 4 points.

EXAMPLE:

Player One   Player Two

six thousand thirty   six thousand thirty

Tie: "six thousand thirty"

Tie Breaker:

Player One   Player Two

three thousand ten   seven thousand sixty

Player Two receives 4 points because they have the largest number and it is greater than 6 030. Both players could earn 4 points in the tie breaker if both are greater than the tied number. Play continues until one player earns 50 points.

VARIATION I: Play with three dice per player and build six-digit numbers. The greatest possible number would be 909 090 (nine hundred nine thousand ninety).

VARIATION II: Build a four-digit number with cards. The player with the greater number earns a point.

VARIATION III: Build the least number possible and compare. The player with the least number earns a point.

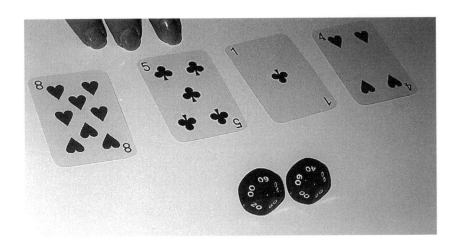

DOUBLE ROUND UP SNAP

LEVEL:	Grade 3 - 7
SKILLS:	Rounding to the nearest 10, 100, or 1 000
PLAYERS:	Teacher vs. Whole Class
EQUIPMENT:	Cards King - 9 (King = 0, Ace = 1), paper, pencil
GETTING STARTED:	Have all students get out a recording sheet and set it up as follows:

MY NUMBER	ROUNDED TO	TEACHER'S TARGET

The teacher sets the pace for the game (i.e. the time students are given to record their work). The teacher begins by calling out, "Build your number." Each player turns over two cards from their deck, makes a two-digit number, and records it. The teacher now calls out, "Rounded to...". Each player then rounds their number to the nearest ten and records their rounded number.

The teacher now rolls the target. All players whose rounded number matches the teacher's target earn 2 points. It is easiest for players to circle or check their points off as they play.

EXAMPLE:

MY NUMBER	ROUNDED TO	TEACHER'S TARGET
64	60	20
38	(40)	40
	*2 points	

VARIATION:

For play rounding to the nearest 100.

Players draw three cards and round to the nearest 100.

624 rounded to 600.

Teacher rolls the target with one ten-sided die being the 100's and one decadie. The teacher must also round their target.

670 is rounded to 700.

For play rounding to the nearest 1 000.

Players draw four cards and round to the nearest 1 000.

7 962 is rounded to 8 000.

Teacher rolls the target with two decadice. The teacher must also round their target.

4 090 is rounded to 4 000.

91

Double Round Up Snap

① Build Tens #   ② Round to the nearest 10

③ Record it   ④ Wait for the target

⑤ If you match keep cards in
your point pile

My #	Rounded To	Target	
64	60	50	
44	40	00	
24	20	70	
44	40	30	
89	90	10	
58	60	40	
35	40	40✓	
67	70	10	
78	80	30	
89	90	10	
10	10	60	
24	20	50	
44	40	60	
15	20	00	
18	20	70	
81	80	30	
54	50	60	
71	30	90	
43	40	00	
51	60	20	(CASSIE) Gr - 5
64	70	20	

My #	round	target	score
955	1000	700	
836	800	200	
249	400	200	
427	400	1000	
918	120	100	
955	100	100	
385	400	400	11
338	300	300	11
644	600	200	
249	200	600	
597	600	600	11
508	500	500	11
795	800	600	
138	100	1000	11
644	600	1000	
942	900	800	
815	800	800	11
795	800	200	
308	300	200	

Justin Taylor
gr 6

Katie Scott
gr 6

My #	Rounded	Target	Score
823	800	700	0
892	900	200	0
721	700	700	2
972	1000	100	2
882	900	100	0
963	1000	100	0
932	900	400	0
646	600	100	0
321	300	300	2
227	200	300	0
559	600	600	2
223	200	600	0
430	400	500	0
442	5100	600	0
321	300	100	0
524	500	1000	0
836	800	800	2

PLACE VALUE SHOWDOWN

LEVEL: Grade 3 - 6

SKILLS: Comparing numbers 0 - 9 090

PLAYERS: 2 - 4

EQUIPMENT: Cards King - 9, (King = 0, Ace = 1)

GETTING STARTED: Players divide the deck evenly. At the beginning of each turn, players turn over four cards and build a three or four-digit number (if a zero is the first card turned over, then the number built will be a hundreds number). Numbers are built from left to right as the cards are turned over. Both players now verbalize their numbers.

EXAMPLE:

Player One	Player Two

"six thousand four hundred seventy two"	"five thousand nine hundred sixty three"

After both players have built their numbers, the two decadice are rolled, the first being the thousands/hundreds position and the second being the tens/ones position.

Roll   "six thousand eighty"

Players now compare their number to the number rolled. Players who have built a number greater than the number rolled place these cards into their point pile.

In the example above, Player One earns all of the cards played.

If both players have a number greater than the number rolled, each player places their own cards into their own point pile.

Play continues with players building new numbers and re-rolling the decadice.

VARIATION: Players build their numbers and roll the decadice. To earn the cards, players must have a number less than the decadice.

EXAMPLE:

Player One

Cards: 0, 3, 6, 2
"three hundred sixty two"

Player Two

Cards: 2, 6, 3, 3
"two thousand six
hundred thirty three"

Roll: 10, 20 = 1 020
    "one thousand twenty"

Only Player One earns the cards.

THOUGHT PROVOKERS:

1. About how often do players earn their own cards?

2. Is it more or less likely that both players will earn cards at the same time?

3. Would players be more successful if they could manipulate their cards when building their numbers? Why or why not?

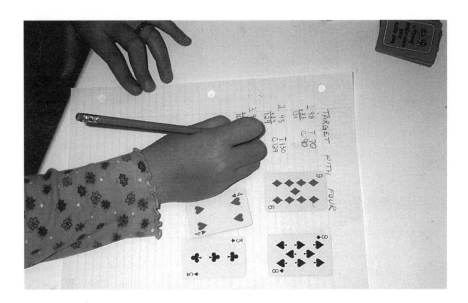

95

A TARGET ROUND

LEVEL: Grade 3 - 7

SKILLS: Comparing and building numbers to 9 090, rounding to the nearest thousands
Variation: Comparing and building numbers to 909 090, rounding to the nearest hundred thousands.

PLAYERS: 2 - 4

EQUIPMENT: Cards King - 9 (King = 0, Ace = 1), two or three decadice, gameboard (see reproducibles), paper, pencil

GETTING STARTED: Play begins by rolling the two decadice and players cooperatively make a thousands number for their target (e.g. 8 010 = eight thousand ten). Players are now dealt four cards each.

Players arrange their cards to build a number that when rounded to the nearest thousand is closest to the target.

EXAMPLE: Player One's cards: 5, 4, 2, 0 - rounded to 5 000.

Player Two's cards: 2, 1, 8, 7 - makes 8 172 rounded to 8 000.

Player Two earns 1 point for being closest to the target. In the event of a tie (i.e. both players' numbers are equally close to the target) both players earn a point. The dice are re-rolled for a new target and players are dealt four new cards. Play continues for a set period of time. The player with the most points is the winner.

TEACHING TIP: Have players record their numbers rounded to and the target number.

THOUGHT PROVOKERS:

1. Does it make any difference as to whether you make your number before or after the other players? Explain.

2. Describe the rule for rounding to a younger player. Explain any techniques you use to make rounding easier.

3. Were there any rounds where both players made rounded numbers with their cards that were equally as close to the target roll? How often did this happen?

96

VARIATION: For practice up to 909 090 each player is dealt six cards. At the same time, three decadice are rolled to set the target (players do this cooperatively). Players build numbers into the hundred thousands place, that when rounded to the nearest hundred thousand is closest to the target.

EXAMPLE: Target: 608 030

Player One builds 587 324 and rounds to 600 000.

Use the same Thought Provokers as in the original rules (see above).

SOMETHING TO TRY: Try playing as follows and discuss the new Thought Provokers.

Players are dealt the appropriate number of cards. They do not rearrange them. The first card is placed into the highest place value holder, the next card the second highest, etc.

EXAMPLE:

The number is then rounded to the nearest thousand (e.g. 6 971 is rounded to 7 000).

Two decadice are now rolled. The player with the rounded number closest to the target earns a point.

THOUGHT PROVOKERS:

1. How often do you think you will tie with other players?

2. If you could have rearranged your cards in this game do you think you would be more successful in being closer to the target?

ADVANCED VARIATION: We tried this in Grade 5, 6 and 7 and experienced some excellent results. Try playing as follows and discuss the accompanying Thought Provokers.

Each player is dealt six cards and players may choose to arrange them in any order. Once players freeze their numbers, they round them to the nearest 100 000.

The dice are then rolled to establish the target. Players now compare their rounded number to the target. The player with the rounded number nearest the target earns 1 point.

 **TEACHING TIP:** Players need to think about the probability of the roll over time. This will help them to develop strategy for building their numbers so they maximize their chances of scoring.

THOUGHT PROVOKERS:

1. What strategy did you use when arranging your cards when you first started playing? Did it change over time? Explain.

2. What place value holders do you consider to be the most important when building your number and why?

3. What advice would you give to a new player for maximizing their chances for building numbers closest to the target?

Remember: To make good predictions it helps to consider previous rounds of play and the combinations that happened.

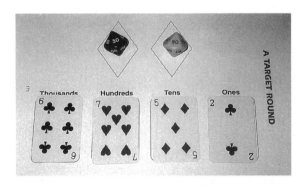

ROCK N' ROLLERS

LEVEL: Grade 4 - 7

SKILLS: Creating six-digit or eight-digit numbers, reading large numbers, comparing numbers

PLAYERS: 2

EQUIPMENT: Two decadice per player and two ten-sided (0-9) dice per player

GETTING STARTED: All players roll their assortment of dice at the same time. Players then begin arranging their dice to make the largest number possible. The first player to finish calls out "Rock N Roll" and verbalizes their number to the other players. All other players must freeze their numbers in their current order, even if they are not finished arranging them.

NOTE: Four dice create 100 000's numbers

If the first player done is also the player with the greatest number of the group they earn 10 points. If not, they earn 0 points for that round. The player who does have the greatest number of the group would earn 5 points, provided they verbalize it correctly. All other players earn 0. The first player to earn 50 points is the winner.

EXAMPLE: Player One:

Rearranges dice: = 962 000

Player Two:

Rearranges dice: = 644 030

Player Three:

Rearranges dice: = 860 602

Player Two verbalizes "Rock N' Roll" first and says, "six hundred forty four thousand thirty." The player earns no points, since this is not the greatest number.

Player One earns 5 points (after reading their number properly), since 962 000 was the largest number rolled of the group.

 **TEACHING TIP:**

Seeing place value represented in a variety of ways (as in the mixture of dice) helps children practice grouping or "chunking" in threes.

i.e. ones, tens, hundreds "chunk",
    thousands, ten thousands, hundred thousands

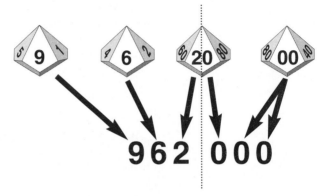

DRIVING RANGE

LEVEL: Grade 4 - 7

SKILLS: Logical reasoning, problem solving, place value, probability

PLAYERS: 2

EQUIPMENT: Two decadice, paper, pencil, gameboard (see reproducibles)

GETTING STARTED: To begin, Player One secretly rolls both decadice. If the dice are the exact same number, then one die is re-rolled (there must be at least a ten number range between both numbers).

Player Two now begins by guessing any two-digit number. The goal of the game is to guess the "hidden range" (i.e. the two numbers rolled on the dice) in the fewest guesses possible. Every guess is counted as 1 point against that player. Just like in golf, a low score is best. After Player Two makes a guess (e.g. "Does 48 fit in the range?"), Player One must verbalize whether this number fits into the hidden range. Player One's response will give Player Two some information as to what the hidden range might be.

EXAMPLE: Player One secretly rolls:

Player Two makes a guess: "Does 48 fit in the range?"

Player One replies: "Yes, it fits."

Player Two now guesses what they think the hidden range is: "Is it 20 to 50?"

Player One replies: "No, it is not."

Player Two is incorrect, so they can now guess a new number to see whether or not this new guess will fit the range.

Player Two makes a guess: "Does 35 fit the range?"

Player One responds: "No, it does not."

Player Two can now assume that the range starts at 40 and ends somewhere higher. Player Two has now eliminated several ranges.

Player Two now guesses a new range: "Is it 40 to 70?"

Player One responds: "No, it is not."

Player Two now makes their third number guess: "Does 62 fit in the range?"

Player One responds: "No, it does not."

Now Player Two can reason that the range must either be 40 to 50 or 40 to 60, as 62 was too high.

Player Two now guesses the range to be 40 to 60.

Player One responds: "Yes!"

Player Two earns 3 points; 1 point for each of their three guesses.

The winner is the player with the least accumulated points (guesses) at the end of several rounds.

Player Two's gameboard from the above example is shown below.

	Guess Any Number	Does it fit the range?	Guess The Range	Is this the range?	Other Possibilities
1.	48	yes	20 - 50?	no	30 - 50? 10 - 80?
2.	35	no	40 - 70?	no	40 - 90? 40 - 60?
3.	62	no	40 - 60?	yes	
4.					
5.					

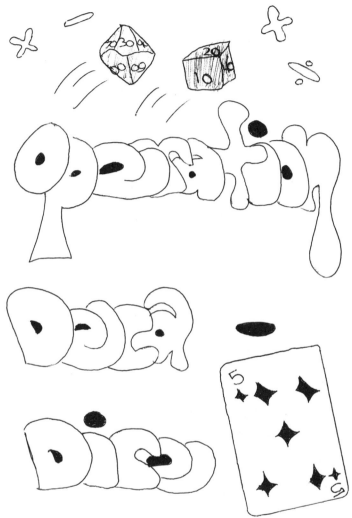

The Operations

ROLL A 100

LEVEL: Grade 1 - 3 (Variation: Grade 2 - 5)

SKILLS: Adding 10's to 100, probability

PLAYERS: 2 - 4

EQUIPMENT: Four decadice, gameboard (see reproducibles), pencil

GETTING STARTED: The goal of the game is to find numbers that when added, equal the sum of 100.

EXAMPLE:

Round One

Player One rolls:

Player One selects 80 + 20 = 100 and earns 2 points.

Player Two rolls:

Player Two selects 50 + 50 = 100 and earns 2 points.

Round Two

Players may combine more than two dice to equal 100. For example:

Player One rolls:

Player One selects 50 + 40 + 10 = 100 and earns 3 points.

Players may have two separate combinations to earn 4 points. For example:

Player Two rolls:

Player Two selects 80 + 20 = 100 and 40 + 60 = 100 and earns 4 points.

Round Three

Players earn an additional 2 bonus points if all four die equal 100. For example:

Player One rolls:

Player One selects 20 + 30 + 40 + 10 = 100 and earns 4 points plus 2 bonus points for a total of 6 points.

Players continue to alternate rolling the dice. In the event that a player rolls no combinations that equal 100, the player earns 0 points for that round.

e.g.  (This can happen!)

The first player to earn 50 points wins.

VARIATION: Players roll all four dice once. They may select any dice to freeze and re-roll the other dice to a maximum of three rolls. Players are trying to create a three or four-addend combination to equal 100. Players strike out if they go over 100. Players may freeze after any roll.

EXAMPLE: Player One rolls:

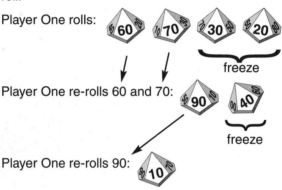

Player One re-rolls 60 and 70:

freeze

Player One re-rolls 90:

At this point, Player One has:

Player One verbalizes "10 + 40 + 30 + 20 = 100" and earns 6 points (4 points plus 2 bonus points).

Players must alternate who goes first each round.

THOUGHT PROVOKERS:

1. How many different combinations (on the four decadice) would result in no sums of 100? Predict and then set your dice to figure out the combinations.

2. With a partner roll out 25 combinations of four decade numbers and record all that have no sums of 100. Compare your findings with another group. Were there more or less than you expected? Explain.

PICK A FACT... ANY FACT

LEVEL: Grade 1 - 3

SKILLS: Adding 10's and 1's without regrouping, comparing sums

PLAYERS: 2 or more

EQUIPMENT: One decadie per player, cards Ace - 9 (Ace = 1), one regular die

GETTING STARTED: Step One:

One player flips over the top card of the deck. All players now roll their own decadie and add this number to the number on the card. Players alternate verbalizing their math sentence.

EXAMPLE:

Step One:

Player One flips:

Player One rolls: and verbalizes: "Thirty plus nine equals thirty nine."

Player Two rolls: and verbalizes: "Eighty plus nine equals eighty nine."

Step Two:

To determine who earns the cards, players alternate rolling the regular die. If an odd number is rolled (i.e. 1, 3 or 5) then the player who rolled the least sum earns the cards. If an even number is rolled (i.e. 2, 4 or 6) then the player who rolled the greatest sum earns the cards.

In the above example, players roll a 5 (which is odd), therefore Player One earns the cards and verbalizes "39 is less than 89".

In the event of a tie (i.e. both players have the same sum) both players keep their own card and place it into their point pile.

THOUGHT PROVOKERS:

1. Do you think this game is fair? Why or why not?

2. Would it be fair if you took out step two and the winner was determined by the player who had the greatest sum always earning the cards?

3. Is there an equal chance of rolling an odd or even number on the regular die?

STRIKING DICE

LEVEL: Grade 2 - 6

SKILLS: Adding 10's and 1's to 100, probability

PLAYERS: 2 or teams of 2 vs. 2

EQUIPMENT: Two decadice, two ten-sided (0-9) dice, paper, pencil

GETTING STARTED: The goal of the game is for players to get a sum as close to 100 as possible without going over. Players alternate turns rolling the dice. Player One begins by selecting and rolling either a decadie or ten-sided die. Players add their numbers as they go. A player may choose to stop after their second, third or final fourth roll. The player with the sum closest to 100 without going over wins the round and earns a point. Players earn 5 points for reaching 100 exactly.

EXAMPLE: Player One's first roll (chooses a decadie):

Player One's second roll (chooses a decadie):

 50 + 40 = 90

Player One's third roll (chooses a ten-sided die):

 90 + 8 = 98

Player One "freezes" with an accumulative sum of 98.

Player Two's first roll (chooses a decadie):

Player Two's second roll (chooses a decadie):

70 + 80 = 150

Player Two "strikes out" with a sum of 150. Player One wins the round and earns 1 point.

THOUGHT PROVOKERS:

1. Which dice are the best to start with? Explain your reasoning.

2. About how many rolls does it usually take to get close to 100?

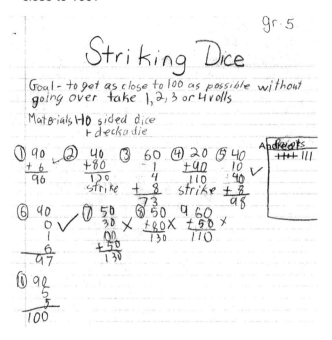

gr. 5

Striking Dice

Goal - to get as close to 100 as possible without going over take 1, 2, 3 or 4 rolls

Materials 10 sided dice
+ deck a die

① 90
+ 6
96

② 40
+80
120
strike

③ 60
- 1
4
+ 8
73

④ 20
+90
110
strike

⑤ 40
10
40
+ 8
98 ✓

Andrew's
+++ |||

⑥ 40
0
1
6
97 ✓

⑦ 50
30
00
+50
130 ✗

⑧ 50
+80 ✗
130

⑨ 60
+50 ✗
110

⑩ 92
5
3
100

111

In the game striking dice the best opening dice is the deckadie. Because you get a good start and you can not strike out and the game molds it's self from theire.

Some of the skills implyed are addition and probobility.

I took risks on the second roll because if the first roll was 60 or less, I used the decadie.

On the 3rd roll if my acumulative total was 60 or less I rolled the decadie again. If it was 70 or more I used the 10 sided

On the fourth roll I did the same stradagey as the 3rd roll

You can't have more than 4 rolls.

I like having my opponent go first so I can set a target of how high I need to go.

Andrea

Menzies

112

TWO HUNDRED

LEVEL:	Grade 3 - 6
SKILLS:	Probability, adding 10's to 200, mental math Variation: subtracting/adding 10's to 200
PLAYERS:	2
EQUIPMENT:	One decadie, gameboard (see reproducibles), pencil
GETTING STARTED:	To begin, each player needs their own gameboard as shown below.

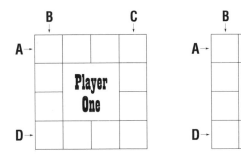

The goal of the game is to build an accumulative total of 200 on each side. Players alternate rolling their die. Players select the best place for that number and record it in their gameboard. Once a number is recorded it cannot be changed. Players roll and record their own numbers.

EXAMPLE: Shown below is a sample round with both players gameboards completed.

	B		C	
A→	10	60	20	80	=170
	70	**Player**		10
	20	**One**		80
D→	90	00	80	30	=200
	‖		‖	
	190		200	

	B		C	
A→	20	00	20	80	=120
	10	**Player**		20
	40	**Two**		30
D→	80	20	20	60	=180
	‖		‖	
	150		190	

Players compare their totals for each side. Players closest to 200 earn 1 point for that side.

If players tie, they both earn a point. Players who reach 200 exactly earn 2 points.

In the previous example, Player One earns 6 points and Player Two earns no points.

 **TEACHING TIP:** This game is very similar to Square Doubling in "Dice Works" (Box Cars - Volume III). The cross over for doing mental math, adding and subtracting tens makes this game a "keeper".

THOUGHT PROVOKERS:

1. Are some numbers better placed in corners than others?

2. Mental math extensions:
   Did you know?
   10 + 20 + 30 + 40 = 100
   20 + 40 + 60 + 80 = 200

3. How can these patterns help you with your number placement?

4. Make a class chart of all the combinations rolled that equal 200.

5. How many possible combinations are there?

VARIATION: To increase the level of difficulty have players play with the option of adding and/or subtracting integers to target 200 (e.g. 80 + 60 - 20 + 80 = 200). Players could also make a class chart of all the adding integer combinations that, when rolled, equal 200. Do you think there would be more or less than just addition?

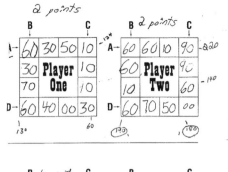

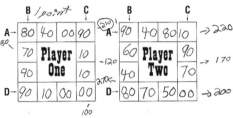

61

"200"

Jason
gr 5
E.B.

How many games did I play? 4

How many games did I win? 1 win, 3 ties 0 loses

Did I get a perfect game? No

we figured out the chance of having a perfect
one was $\frac{5}{16} = \frac{1}{3}$ chances.

what Scores = 200

$80+10+20+90=200$

$10+40+70+80=200$

$20+40+60+80=200$

$80+60+30+30=200$

$80+70+30+20=200$

$50+50+50+50=200$

You should put them so if you put
one number in the corner it could make
200 twice. To add to 200 in your head

That the point of the game was gets 1 point and
to get closest to 200 wins if you do you
get 200 exactly you get 2 points

115

① How many games did I play? #4

② How many games did I win? _None_

③ Did you get a perfect game? _No_

④ We figured out the chance of having a Perfect game was $\frac{5}{16}$ or $\frac{1}{3}$ Chances.

⑤ What scores = 200?

① 50 50 50 50 = 200

② 60 60 40 40 = 200

③ 60 70 20 50 = 200

④ 70 70 00 60 = 200

⑤ 80 20 50 50 = 200

⑥ 90 80 30 00 = 200

⑦ 50 50 90 10 = 200

⑧ 80 40 20 10 = 200   60 60 50 30

116

HITTING BENCHMARKS

LEVEL: Grade 3 - 6

SKILLS: Adding 10's to 1 000, probability, predicting

PLAYERS: 4 - 6

EQUIPMENT: Two decadice, paper, pencil, calculators (optional to check for accuracy)

GETTING STARTED: The goal of the game is for players to predict the number of times a "benchmark" will be hit exactly during the round. The benchmark numbers are 100, 200, 300, 400, etc. on route to 1 000. If agreed upon prior to the start of the round, benchmark numbers can be changed (e.g. 100, 150, 200, 250, 300, etc.).

Play begins by having all players record their prediction. The first player in the group rolls the two decadice and adds the two numbers. This sum is recorded by all the players. The next player rolls the two decadice. All players add these numbers and add this new sum to get an accumulated total. Players continue alternating rolling the dice until the accumulated total is over 1 000.

At the end of the round players determine how many "benchmarks" were hit and which player made the closest prediction. The player with the closest prediction is the winner.

EXAMPLE: Possible predictions for players might be the following:

Player One's Prediction: 6

Player Two's Prediction: 8

Player Three's Prediction: 2

Player Four's Prediction: 4

			Accum. Total
Player One:		$60 + 30 = 90$	90
Player Two:		$00 + 20 = 20$	110
Player Three:		$60 + 70 = 130$	240
Player Four:		$40 + 30 = 70$	310
Player One:		$00 + 60 = 60$	370
Player Two:		$90 + 40 = 130$	500
Player Three:		$30 + 60 = 90$	590

Benchmark

And so on...

Once players have reached 1 000, they check and compare their predictions to determine the winner.

THOUGHT PROVOKERS:

Play several rounds. How often are benchmarks hit on 100, 200, 300, etc? How does this change when the benchmarks are changed to 50, 100, 150, 200, 250?

VARIATION:

Players begin with 1 000, roll two dice, add them, then subtract this total from 1 000. Continue subtracting down to 0.

 TEACHING TIP:

Encourage players to try this variation as subtraction is often more difficult.

118

DECIDEDLY DIFFERENT

LEVEL: Grade 2 - 6

SKILLS: Subtracting 10's, probability, adding 10's, developing an outcome chart

PLAYERS: 2 - 4

EQUIPMENT: Two decadice, paper, pencil, outcome chart for post play (see reproducibles)

GETTING STARTED: The goal of the game is to be the first player to accumulate a sum of 200 or greater. Players must take an even number of turns.

Player One starts by rolling the two decadice and subtracting the numbers. If the difference is not 0 or 10, the player gets the number of points rolled.

e.g. roll   70 - 00 = 70 points

The player may roll again to attempt to accumulate more points or freeze and protect them. On each turn a player may take as many rolls as they like until they either roll a difference of 10 or 0 and strike out or choose to stop, freeze and protect their accumulated points.

If a player continues to roll and they roll a difference of 0 or 10 they lose any points they may have earned on that turn and were not protected. The first player to earn 200 or over after an even amount of turns have been taken, is the winner.

EXAMPLE: **Player One's Turn:**

First Roll: 90 - 60 = 30 points

Second Roll: 50 - 00 = 50 points
accumulative total = 80

Third Roll: 30 - 10 = 20 points
accumulative total = 100

Fourth Roll: 70 - 60 = 10
Since Player One rolled a difference of 10, they lose all their points for this turn.

Player Two's Turn:

First Roll: 80 - 10 = 70 points

Second Roll: 70 - 40 = 30 points
accumulative total = 100

Third Roll: 60 - 20 = 40 points
accumulative total = 140

Player Two chooses to "freeze" here and has earned 140 points that now count as their starting point for their next turn.

Player One's Turn:

First Roll: 90 - 10 = 80 points

Second Roll: 30 - 30 = 0
Player One loses their 80 points and returns back to 0.

Player Two's Turn:

First Roll: 70 - 20 = 50 points
accumulative total = 190
(140 from first turn + 50)

Second Roll: 60 - 10 = 50 points
accumulative total = 240

Since both players have had an even number of turns and Player Two has reached an accumulative total over 200, Player Two wins the round.

120

THOUGHT PROVOKERS:

1. Can the game be won on the first turn? If so, about how often would this happen? How many rolls would a player need? What would be the fewest number of rolls that would be needed? The average number of rolls that would be needed?

2. How often does a difference of 0 or 10 happen? How did you find out? How does this information help you to decide to roll or freeze and protect your accumulated sum/points?

3. Develop the outcome chart for this game (see page 220 for chart).

4. Revise the rules to test out an addition or multiplication variation.

 **TEACHING TIP:** Do not give the outcome chart to the students before they play. After they gain experience by playing they will be more prepared to generate and understand it. Start by giving them an empty chart and ask, " How many ways can you get a difference of 0, 10, 20?" and so on.

VARIATION: Have the players continue to a higher accumulative total (e.g. 500 or 1 000). This may affect how some of the thought provokers will be answered.

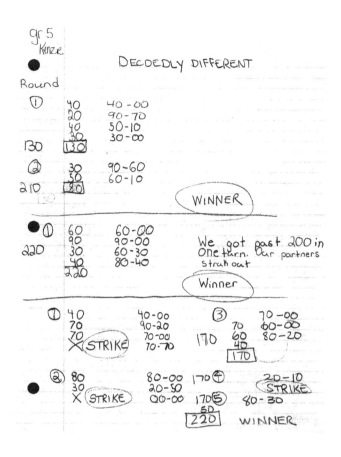

gr 5
Kinzie

DECDEDLY DIFFERENT

Round

①   40   40 - 00
      20   90 - 70
      40   50 - 10
      30   30 - 00
130   130

②   30   90 - 60
      50   60 - 10
210   80   WINNER

①   60   60 - 00
      90   90 - 00   We got past 200 in
220 30   60 - 30   one turn. Our partners
      40   80 - 40   struk out
    220
                  Winner

① 40   40 - 00   ③   70 - 00
  70   90 - 20   70   60 - 00
  70   70 - 00   170 60   80 - 20
  X STRIKE   70 - 70   40
                            170

② 80   80 - 00   170 ④   20 - 10
  30   20 - 50   STRIKE
  X STRIKE   00 - 00   170 ⑤   80 - 30
                      50
                220   WINNER

TARGET WITH FOUR

LEVEL: Grade 2 - 6

SKILLS: Adding two-digit numbers with regrouping
                      Variation: Subtracting two-digit numbers with
                      regrouping

PLAYERS: 2 - 4

EQUIPMENT: Cards King - 9 (King = 0, Ace = 1), paper, pencil

GETTING STARTED: Each player takes four cards and makes a two-digit
                      plus a two-digit sum. Regrouping is allowed.

EXAMPLE:

Player One	Player Two
1 3 5	1 0 6

One player rolls the two decadice and adds them for a
sum.

e.g.   60 + 30 = 90

The player with the sum closest to the rolled sum
earns the cards. In the example above, Player Two is
closer to 90 and earns all the cards and places these
into their point pile.

VARIATION: Roll the target sum first.

Allow players to either add or subtract their two-digit
numbers in attempt to "hitting" the rolled target sum.
For example, if a low target is rolled (20 + 10 = 30)
players may find subtraction a better operation to use.
The player closest to the target (they can be over and
still closest to) earns all the cards.

One player rolls the two decadice and adds them for a sum.

e.g. 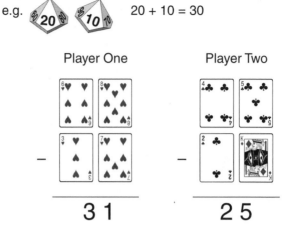 20 + 10 = 30

Player One   Player Two

−   −

3 1   2 5

Player One earns all the cards.

TARGET WITH FOUR

1. 98   T=70 D26
   +33   C=90
   131

2. 95   T=130 D1
   +34   C=⟨29⟩
   129

3. 91   T=70 D25
   +17   C=95
   108

4. 98   T=180 D39
   43   C=⟨141⟩
   141

5. 63   T=160 D18
   +79   C=⟨142⟩
   142

6. 89   T=40 D53
   +44   C=93
   133

7. 75   T=80 D15
   +43   C=95
   118

8. 71   T=70 D09
   +11   C=61
   82

9. 93   T=140 D1
   +26   C=141
   119

10. 38   T=160 D60
    +29 C=100
    67

Andrea Kenzie
Gr.5

D= DIFFERENCE
My CODE   T=TARGET   C=CLOSEST TO

Target With Four

In the game target with four my plan was to make a number from 80-100. Because it is the middle of 00-180. Whenever I got a boxcars bonus I used it to make my tens 90. Here are some averages.

- The average winner was 109.
- The average target was 110.
- The aveage difference was 19.

The points despersed themselves evenly I got 3, my opponent got 3, the other opponent got four.

Nobody got exactly on the target in our game, but in two rounds it was off by 10

Andrea Kenzie
Gr. 5

TARGET WITH FOUR

1. 74
   +50
   ───
   124
   TARGET = 70
   CLOSEST TO: 90

2. 40
   +30
   ───
    70
   T = 130
   C = 129

3. 93
   +02
   ───
    95
   T = 70
   C = 95

4. 74
   +50
   ───
   124
   T = 180
   C = 151

5. 99
   +38
   ───
   137
   T = 160
   C = 142

6. 85
   +11
   ───
    96
   T = 40
   C = 93

7. 14
   +98
   ───
   112
   T = 80
   C = 95

8. 98
   +17
   ───
   113
   T = 70
   C = 61

9. 74
   +69
   ───
   141
   T = 140
   C = 141

10. 88
   +12
   ───
   100
   T = 160
   C = 100

125

NASTY NINETIES

(submitted by Marie Sternberg - class of 2000 Grade 5, England)

LEVEL: Grade 3 - 6

SKILLS: Adding multiples of 10 to 1 000, subtracting 90, probability

PLAYERS: 2

EQUIPMENT: Two decadice, paper, pencil

GETTING STARTED: Players alternate rolling the decadice, adding them and recording their sum. When the two dice are rolled, players add each succeeding total. However, rolling a sum of 90, is a "Nasty Roll". If a sum of 90 is rolled, the 90 must be subtracted from the total. Play continues until one player reaches or exceeds 1 000.

EXAMPLE:

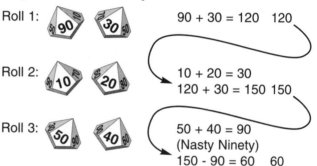

Player One's Rolls Only: **Score**

Roll 1:   90 + 30 = 120   120

Roll 2:   10 + 20 = 30
               120 + 30 = 150 150

Roll 3:   50 + 40 = 90
               (Nasty Ninety)
               150 - 90 = 60   60

etc...

Should a player roll a sum of 90 to start, they can either record it as -90 (if familiar with negative numbers) or subtract it as soon as they have a score high enough to do so.

THOUGHT PROVOKERS:

1. What is the probability of rolling a combination that equals 90?

2. Develop the outcome chart to prove your answer.

126

Nasty Nineties

Goal: To be the first to reach 1000
Skill: adding 10's with regrouping
Players: 2
Equip: 2 decadice per player
Getting
Started: Roll 2 dice ⊕, accumulate your sum.
  ★ Nasty Roll = ⊖ _____
     you must minus 90 if your sum is 90

Round	Sum	Accumulated Sum
1	70	70
2	110	180
3	130	310
4	20	330
5	70	400
6	120	520
7	110	630
8	130	760
9	-90	670
10	70	740
11	50	790
12	40	830
13	160	990
14	100	1900 ✗ ✗
15		

Sean Fonner

I Won!

Nasty Nineties Thought Provokers

1. How many rolls to reach 1000?
How many times did a Nasty Ninety
happen? It took me 14 rolls and I got
1 nasty 90

2. Develop the outcomes chart for
this game. How many total
outcomes are there? How many
outcomes that equal 90? How
does this fraction/ratio compare
to what actually happened in your
game? There are a possible 100
outcomes. The one with the most
combos was 90, yet I only got 1.
The 2 least common ones 00 and 180
weren't rolled between the two of us.
There is a 10:100 ratio, or a
1:10 ratio for 90's.

What   1 rolled
Happened ─────── = 7% rolled   10
          14   ─── chance = 10% chance
                          100

127

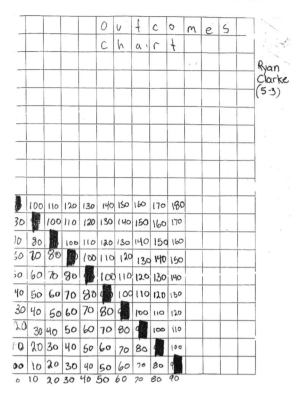

Outcomes chart

Ryan Clarke (5-3)

100	110	120	130	140	150	160	170	180
30	100	110	120	130	140	150	160	170
10	80	100	110	120	130	140	150	160
50	70	80	100	110	120	130	140	150
50	60	70	80	100	110	120	130	140
40	50	60	70	80	100	110	120	130
30	40	50	60	70	80	100	110	120
20	30	40	50	60	70	80	100	110
10	20	30	40	50	60	70	80	100
00	10	20	30	40	50	60	70	80	9

0 10 20 30 40 50 60 70 80 90

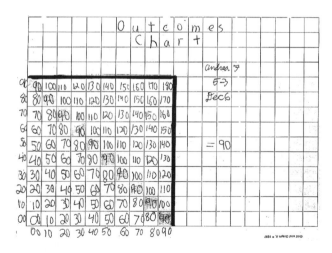

Outcomes Chart

andrea 7
5-3
Dec 6

= 90

90	90	100	110	120	130	140	150	160	170	180
80	80	90	100	110	120	130	140	150	160	170
70	70	80	90	100	110	120	130	140	150	160
60	60	70	80	90	100	110	120	130	140	150
50	50	60	70	80	90	100	110	120	130	140
40	40	50	60	70	80	90	100	110	120	130
30	30	40	50	60	70	80	90	100	110	120
20	20	30	40	50	60	70	80	90	100	110
10	10	20	30	40	50	60	70	80	90	100
00	00	10	20	30	40	50	60	70	80	90

00 10 20 30 40 50 60 70 80 90

Class ratios

Ashleig
Ellis
(5-

$\frac{1}{12} = .083$ $\frac{1}{14} .071$ $\frac{3}{12} .25$

$\frac{2}{18} .111$ $\frac{1}{12} .083$ $\frac{0}{6} .0$

$\frac{0}{8} .0$ $\frac{1}{6} .166$ $\frac{0}{13} .0$

$\frac{0}{11} .0$ $\frac{1}{11} .090$

12%

Our class results
Nasty Ninetics

ONE HUNDRED EIGHTY

(submitted by Marie Sternberg - class of 2000 Grade 5, England)

LEVEL: Grade 4 - 7

SKILLS: Adding and subtracting multiples of 10; doubling and tripling numbers, probability

PLAYERS: 2

EQUIPMENT: One regular die, one decadie, paper, pencil

GETTING STARTED: The goal of the game is for players to bullseye 180. Player One rolls both dice. The regular die indicates whether the number on the decadie should be doubled, tripled or left as it is (i.e. single).

 single

 double

 triple

This number is then added to or subtracted from the player's score, aiming for a target of 180. When the target is reached, the player says, "One hundred eighty" (in a drawled out voice) and earns 1 point.

EXAMPLE:

Player Two's Rolls		Math Sentence	Accumulative Score
Roll 1:		$1 \times 10 = 10$	10
(single)			
Roll 2:		$3 \times 40 = 120$ $10 + 120 = 130$	130
(triple)			
Roll 3:		$1 \times 80 = 80$ $130 + 80 = 210$	210
(single)			
Roll 4:		$2 \times 60 = 120$ $210 - 120 = 90$	90
(double)			

130

Roll 5:   3 x 30 = 90
                                    90 + 90 = 180   180

(triple)

Player Two verbalizes, "One hundred eighty" and earns 1 point.

Play continues until one player earns 5 points.

NOTE: In Britain, the game of darts is taken very seriously, and televised dart championships run for days or even weeks. British students are very familiar with the phrase "one hundred eighty" (said in almost a drawl) when a player scores the maximum possible with three darts, and this is followed with a round of applause. Scoring for darts also involves doubling and tripling numbers, based on where the board is hit. Hence this game!

THOUGHT PROVOKERS:

1. How many total outcomes are possible?

2. Can you reach the target of 180 in one roll? What is the probability of targeting 180 in one roll?

3. How many rolls did it take you to target 180? How does this compare with your class average?

4. Examine your strategy. Did it change from one game to the next?

 **TEACHING TIP:**   Have the students develop an outcome chart (see student's sample).

One Hundred and Eighty 28/30 Kendra Kerrigan

How many total outcomes are possible?

There are 60 total outcomes 10/10 because there are 30 from 1-3 and if you multiply that by 2, it equals 60.

Can you reach the target of 180 in one roll? What is the chance of doing so?

Yes, you can reach the target of 180 in one roll. You have a 4 out of 60 chance.

9/10

We had 180 reached in two rolls. What possible combinations of rolls could have been rolled?

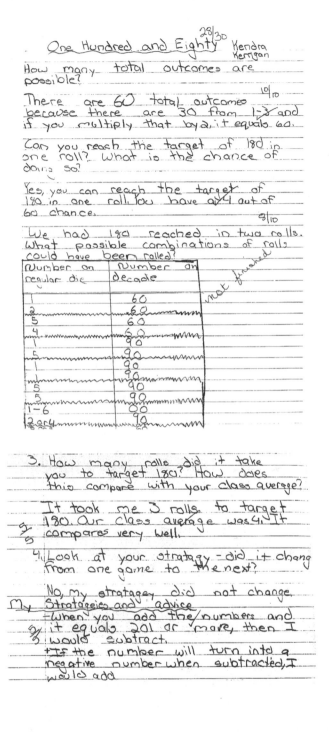

Number on regular die	Number on decade	
1	60	
2	60	
5	60	
4	60	
1	90	
5	90	
1	90	
	90	
5	90	
5	90	
1-6	90	
2 or 4	90	

not finished

3. How many rolls did it take you to target 180? How does this compare with your class average?

It took me 3 rolls to target 180. Our class average was 4. It compares very well. 3/3

4. Look at your strategy - did it change from one game to the next?

No, my strategy did not change.

My Strategies and advice
+When you add the numbers and it equals 201 or more, then I would subtract. 3/3
+If the number will turn into a negative number when subtracted, I would add

132

One Hundred and Eighty

1.b) In all there are sixty different ¹⁹⁄₁₀ outcomes that you could roll. I believe that there are really only thirty because it depends what you roll on the normal die. If you roll a one or a five you leave the number on the decadie. If you roll a two or a four you double the decadie. If you roll a three or a six you triple the decadie. It would be the same as having a die with just one, two and three. If you had a die like that you would get only thirty outcomes. The four five and six just end up repeating the same outcomes as you would get rolling a one, two or three.

2a) You can roll a target of 180 on your first roll two ways. The first is to roll a three or a six and triple sixty. The second is to roll a two or four and double ninety. The chance is two out of thirty or 6.6%.

Normal Die	Decadie	Total	Target	for this question
Roll 1 1	5	90	90	I looked at the
Roll 2 1	5	90	180	outcomes and looked
Roll 1 3	T	90	270	at what all equals
Roll 2 1	S	90	180	180. 9/10
Roll 1 3	T	50	150	
Roll 2 1	S	30	180	There are
Roll 1 1	S	40	40	even more
Roll 2	D	70	180	combinations
Roll 1	S	60	60	
Roll 2 2	D	60	180	
Roll 1 1	3	80	80	
Roll 2 2	D	50	180	

Normal Die	Decadie	Total	Target
Roll 1 3	T	180	240
Roll 2 1	S	60	180
Roll 1 3	T	70	210
Roll 2 1	S	30	180

3. Neither me or my partner reached 180. Our class average was 5 rolls to reach it. We had 18 rounds so I will compare that to the class average. If we had eighteen rounds that is more than 30% higher than the class average.

4. In our game neither of us reached 180. I think if I had gone a little higher and then subtracted the numbers I could have got 180. I ended up a lot of the time going to 30.

To a new player I would suggest to get quite far away from 180 because you generally roll high numbers that you could subtract or add right to 180.

ONE HUNDRED AND EIGHTY

Round	Regular Die		Decadie	Do I ⊕ or ⊖ ?	Sc
1	D	4	120		120
2	D	4	140	+	260
3	S	1	0	+	260
4	S	5	60	-	200
5	F	6	120	-	80
6	S	5	50	+	130
7	S	5	20	+	150
8	S	5	60	+	210
9	F	6	-180	-	20
10	D	0	0	+	20
11	S	1	40	+	60
12	T	3	60	-	120
13	D	2	100	+	220
14	S	5	90	-	130
15	S	1	80	+	210
16	T	3	150	-	60
17	S	1	0	+	60
18	T	6	0	+	60

ONE EIGHTY

	1S	2D	3T	4D	5	6T	
90	90	180	270	180	90	270	90
80	80	160	240	160	80	240	80
70	70	140	210	140	70	210	70
60	60	120	180	120	60	180	60
50	50	100	150	100	50	150	50
40	40	80	120	80	40	120	40
30	30	60	90	60	30	90	30
20	20	40	60	40	20	60	20
10	10	20	30	20	10	30	10
00	00	00	00	00	00	00	00
	1S	2D	3T	4D	5	6T	

Outcomes Chart

134

GOING FOR 500

LEVEL: Grade 3 - 6

SKILLS: Adding with regrouping, decision making, using logical reasoning, probability

PLAYERS: 2 or more

EQUIPMENT: One decadie per player, paper, pencil

GETTING STARTED: Player One begins by rolling their die. Player One must now decide whether to roll again hoping to roll a number greater than that first roll, or freeze and record this number on their paper. If Player One rolls again and is successful in rolling a new number that is greater than their previous roll (it cannot be equal to) then that number is added to their previous number for a new total. If Player One would like to freeze, they can do so, or that player could choose to roll again. If the new number rolled is <u>not</u> greater than the previous number rolled, Player One loses all their accumulated points for that turn.

Players alternate rolling and accumulating their totals until one player reaches and/or exceeds five hundred (500).

EXAMPLE:

Player One

First roll = 40   Player chooses to roll again.

Second roll = 20   Since 20 is less than 40, Player One earns no points.

Player Two

First roll = 10   Player chooses to roll again.

Second roll = 30   Accumulated total = 40
Player chooses to roll again.

Third roll = 70   Player chooses to freeze and records 110 points (on route to 500). (10 + 30 + 70 = 110).

NOTE: These accumulated points are "safe" and can not be "lost" on a future turn.

THOUGHT PROVOKERS:

1. When is it a good decision to freeze and keep your points without taking another roll?

2. Are certain numbers "safer" to roll after? Please explain.

3. Which numbers when rolled will probably give you a higher accumulative total for your turn?

4. Is there any way to get more than 90 points on one turn?

5. What is the maximum number of points you can earn during one turn? Explain.

Alyce 5A

GO FOR 500   SCORESHEET

Total Score	Work Area

1. 0
2. 110
3. 170
    140
     30
    330
5. 380
   140
  6 470
	1. 90 3. 20 5. 60
	             +50 +70
	2. 90 ——— 150
	  +20 70
	 110 6. 50
	           4. 10 90
	            +0 140
	I WIN. 0

1. 110
2. 210
3. 210
    90
   300
4. 300
5. 400
    60
6. 460
    50
  510
	1. 90 2. 10 3. 90 4. 90
	  +20 +90 +90 5 10
	 110 100 +90
	                            100
	6 20 7. 10
	+40 +40 I WIN!
	 60 50

1. 110   2. 310
   140   +80
   230   390
3. 230
   +80
   310
	1. 90 2. 50 3. 10 4. 30
	          90 70 +50
	         140 80 80
	I WIN

page 1

136

Going for 500!   Courtney R
                  Ed. grs

```
  50.
  90.
 140
+80.
 220
 +0.
 -40.
+280
 00.
 -50.
 330
```

When is it good decision to "freeze" and Keep your points without taking another roll?

I think it is a good decision to freeze at 50 because i have 5 chances of losing and 4 chances of winning.

Are certain numbers "safer" to roll after?
00,10,20,30 are "safer" to roll after because numbers higher than that you will not have a big chance to get higher numbers.

Is there any way to get more than 90 points on one turn? Explain. Yes there is because if you roll a 10 then you can roll again and again and again etc. example

10,20,30,40,50,60,70,80,90 = 450

90 = 90

What is the maximum number of points you can score in one turn?   The maximum number you could roll in one turn is 450.

137

A-TEN-SNAP

LEVEL: Grade 2 - 6

SKILLS: Subtracting a one-digit number from a two-digit number using a pattern.

PLAYERS: 2 or more - equal skill level.

EQUIPMENT: Cards King - 9 (King = 0, Ace = 1), one decadie.

 **TEACHING TIP:**   Before play begins, players should practice the "ten take away" strategy in a math warm up. The patterns that make 10 need to be practiced and learned in order to master two-digit subtraction. Teach and have available (if necessary) the following chart:

Start With	Subtract	Think of the Missing Part
10	1	9
10	2	8
10	3	7
10	4	6
10	5	5
10	6	4
10	7	3
10	8	2
10	9	1
10	10	0

The Warm Up Practice

1. Set out a 10 card and leave it out as a visual for students (or set the decadie to show the numeral 10).

2. Players then take turns flipping up a card and practice the "ten take away" strategy.

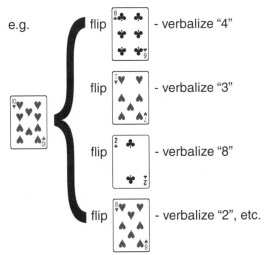

e.g.

flip — verbalize "4"

flip — verbalize "3"

flip — verbalize "8"

flip — verbalize "2", etc.

Once players are confident with this strategy they can begin playing the game.

GETTING STARTED: Player One begins by flipping over the top card of the deck (both players should be mentally using the "ten-take away" strategy). Player One now rolls the decadie for both players to use. Players now subtract the two numbers to calculate the difference. The first player to verbalize the correct difference out loud earns the card. In the event of a tie, players leave the card down and let the pile build. Play then continues until one player gives a correct answer before their opponent and earns all of the accumulated cards. After a set period of time, the winner is the player with the most cards.

 TEACHING TIP: After the winning player has called out the difference, they could then verbalize the entire math sentence (this helps to internalize the math).

EXAMPLE:

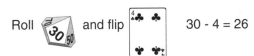

Roll and flip $30 - 4 = 26$

Player verbalizes "Thirty minus four equals twenty six."

THE MISSING DECA

LEVEL: Grade 3 - 6

SKILLS: Adding two-digit numbers, missing addend

PLAYERS: 3 or more

EQUIPMENT: Cards Ace - 9 (Ace = 1), two decadice, paper, pencil (to check for accuracy)

GETTING STARTED: Players alternate turns being the "Roller". The "Roller/Dealer" creates the "secret deca".

The other players are "Guessers". The "Guessers" race against one another to be the first to call out the "secret deca" number.

To begin, the Roller flips up a card to build the "hundreds" part of a number. Then they roll the first decadie which will represent the "tens" part of the number.

Next, the Roller flips up a second card to build the "hundreds" part of the second number, and places this card below the first. The Roller then secretly rolls the second decadie to make the "tens" part of the second number.

The Roller mentally adds these numbers together and verbalizes the sum to the Guessers. The first Guesser to verbalize the "secret deca" earns the cards.

EXAMPLE: Player One is the Roller

Player One flips a card, then rolls a decadie, then flips another card as follows:

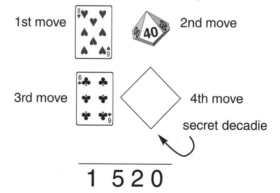

1st move   2nd move

3rd move   4th move

secret decadie

1 5 2 0

Now Player One secretly rolls the "tens" part of the second number, adds the two numbers and verbalizes the sum.

The first player to guess and verbalize the "secret deca" earns the cards. In this example, the first person to guess that Player One rolled an 80 would earn the cards.

 **TEACHING TIP:**

Pay attention to the "tens" part of the first number. It's the most important number to help you solve the missing number.

For instance, in the example above, we know that $8 + 6 = 14$. However, if the sum has 15 hundreds, then the tens part of the number is greater than 9 tens so the missing deca must be at least 60 (leaving 60, 70, 80 and 90 as possibilities). Now think... 40 plus what number equals 120? The answer is 80!

If players need more time to analyze and think about the numbers, change the rules to make this less competitive. Each "Guesser" calculates the answer and records it on their own. All guessers compare their answers and all receive points for correct solutions.

WHO WANTS TO BE A 100 000 AIRE?

LEVEL: Grade 3 - 6

SKILLS: Adding with regrouping to 100 000, probability

PLAYERS: 2

EQUIPMENT: One decadie per player, two ten-sided (0-9) dice, paper (graphing paper if possible), pencil

GETTING STARTED: The goal of the game is to be the first player to reach an accumulative total of one hundred thousand (100 000).

EXAMPLE: Player One begins by rolling all three dice (one decadie and two ten-sided dice) and arranges them to create the largest number possible.

Player One rolls:

Player One verbalizes, "Seven thousand four hundred two (7 402) is the greatest number I can make." Player One now records this number on their paper.

Player Two rolls:

Player Two verbalizes, "Nine thousand sixty one (9 061) is the greatest number I can make." and records this number on their paper.

Player One now takes their second turn.

Player One rolls:

Player One verbalizes, "Four thousand three hundred one (4 301) is the greatest number I can make." Player One now adds this to their previous number for an accumulative total of 11 703.

$$
\begin{array}{r}
7\ 402 \\
+\ 4\ 301 \\
\hline
11\ 703
\end{array}
$$

Play continues until one player reaches or exceeds one hundred thousand!

The following sample shows a complete game played out:

	Player One	Player Two
Roll 1	9 550	7 056
Roll 2	+ 9 520	+ 7 073
	19 070	14 129
Roll 3	+ 8 401	+ 9 630
	27 471	23 759
Roll 4	+ 6 402	+ 3 200
	33 873	26 959
Roll 5	+ 7 400	+ 9 870
	41 273	36 829
Roll 6	+ 6 420	+ 5 502
	47 693	42 321
Roll 7	+ 8 730	+ 8 011
	56 423	50 332
Roll 8	+ 8 100	+ 7 430
	64 523	57 762
Roll 9	+ 5 100	+ 9 610
	69 623	67 372
Roll 10	+ 4 420	+ 8 022
	74 043	75 394
Roll 11	+ 9 601	+ 2 200
	83 644	77 594
Roll 12	+ 9 703	+ 7 302
	93 347	84 896
Roll 13	+ 8 200	+ 8 740
	101 547	93 636

Player One is the "One Hundred Thousandaire" winner!

THOUGHT PROVOKERS:

This is a great game for analyzing data. Have the students use their own rounds of play to work with these questions.

1. About how many rolls do you think it will take to usually reach 100 000? Why? About how many rolls to reach 50 000 (half way)? Does it compare?

2. What percentage of the time were you ahead of your opponent (estimate)? Did the game usually go back and forth with players alternating leads or did one player stay in the lead for most of the game? What do you think is most typical? Explain.

3. Compare your game with some other groups. Describe your comparisons.

4. What was the average roll in your game as you reached your accumulative total to 100 000?

5. Calculate the class average for the number of rolls it took to get to 100 000. Does this compare to your initial prediction and actual results?

144

Who wants to Be a 100 000 Aire?
Questions

1. About how many rolls to reach 100 000? How many rolls to reach halfway? Does it compare?

It took me fifteen rolls to reach one hundred thousand. It only took Mandy fourteen rolls. It took Mandy seven rolls to reach halfway and me about eight(seven and a half really.) The rolls don't compare. —

2. What percentage of the time were you ahead? Did the game usually go back and forth with players alternating leads or did one player lead for most of the game? Compare your answers with some other groups. What do you think is most typical? Explain.

About forty percent of the time, I was ahead. The game was lead by one person then finished by the other.

Groups	Mandy & I	Koryn & Tasia	Erin & Emily
Turns to get to 100 000	Mandy-14 Me-15	Koryn-14 Tasia-14	Erin-13 Emily-14
Lead most of the time	Mandy	Tasia	Erin

In all of the groups, the person with the least number of turns won. The turns it took range between thirteen and fifteen. Those are the typical ones. I think they are typical because you couldn't get one hundred thousand with rolling only six times because it doesn't add up.

3. What is the least and greatest accumulative totals that could be rolled? Could this ever happen?

You could roll all zeros, nine thousand, nine hundred, ninety or it could go on to infinity. Yes this could happen. It could happen because it is a random roll and no one can predict what you will roll.

4. Theoretically, what is the fewest rolls it would take to reach 100 000. Prove it with the math.

The fewest rolls would be eleven.

$$
\begin{array}{r}
9\,990 \\
\times\quad 11 \\
\hline
9\,990 \\
+99\,900 \\
\hline
109\,890
\end{array}
$$

Tasia
Gr.6

145

$\frac{15}{15}$ ★

Who Wants To Be A 100 000 Aire?

1.

To reach 100·000	To reach 50 000	It almost worked out to be exactly half. The difference is 40 044 which is almost half. For the turns it did not turn out quite as well. 3
It took ① tries	It took ① tries	
Total 103 500	Total 37 456	

2. In our game Katie and I were ahead 11/11 times or 100% of the time. For Aylish and Pam, Pam was ahead 100% of the time. For Baily and Melissa was ahead 80% of the time and Baily 20% of the time. For David, David and Zach, David and David were ahead 100% of the time. 4

I think it is typical that is surpose 3 games they are ahead for more than 70% of the time but it is also possible to win when your only ahead for 20% of the time.

3. The least accumulate total you could ever roll is zero because you would keep rolling zero and it would never add up. The highest accumulate total you could get would go into infinty. If you kept on rolling it would just keep on adding up. ⑨

4. The fewest rolls it would take to get to 100 000 would be 11 rolls. I will prove it.

$$\begin{array}{r} 9990 \\ \times\ 11 \\ \hline 9990 \\ 9990 \\ \hline 109890 \end{array}$$

Cam R.
gr. 6

I proved it by getting the highest number you could roll and multiplying it by 11. If I multiplied it by 10 it would be to much and if I multiplied it by 12 it would be too much

4. I think it would take 11 rolls because look 9990 but 10 rolls is 9990

$$\begin{array}{r} 9990 \\ \times 11 \\ \hline 109890 \end{array} \qquad \begin{array}{r} 9990 \\ \times 10 \\ \hline 99900 \end{array} \ 4$$

The number 11 is enough ✓

What was the class avrage for the number it took to get to 100,000 ?

13 ?

146

DECA GOLF

LEVEL:	Grade 4 - 7
SKILLS:	Subtraction with regrouping Variation: division
PLAYERS:	2
EQUIPMENT:	Cards King - 9 (King = 0, Ace = 1), one decadie per player, gameboard (see reproducibles)
GETTING STARTED:	The goal of the game is to have the least accumulative total after nine rounds (holes) of play.

Players divide the deck evenly between themselves. Players will alternate turns throughout the game.

Player One begins by rolling the decadie and recording this number. If 00 is rolled, the player re-rolls the die. The player then flips over one card from the top of their deck and <u>must then</u> decide to record this number in either the tens or ones place value.

EXAMPLE: Player One rolls: and flips:

Player may record:

$$90 \quad \text{or} \quad 90$$
$$-7\square \qquad -\square 7$$

Once a player decides where they will place this number, it is recorded, "frozen" and cannot be changed.

Player One now draws their second card to complete the subtraction sentence.

Player chooses:

$$90$$
$$-7\square$$

and flips a:

Thus:

$$90 - 75 = 15$$

Player One records 15 for their score for the first hole.

Player Two now takes their turn.

Player Two rolls: and flips:

Player records:

$$10 - 9 = 1$$

Player Two does not need to flip up a second card and records a score of 1 for their first hole.

PLAYERS CAN STRIKE AND EARN PENALTIES.

There are times when players will build a subtraction sentence that results in a negative difference. This is not allowed. Players automatically take a 20 point penalty.

EXAMPLE:

Player rolls: and flips:

Since 30 - 70 would result in a negative number, player must choose to put the 7 into the one's place value:

$$30 - \Box7$$

then flips a:

This player earns a strike and records 20 penalty points for the hole.

$$30 - 57$$

STRIKE

148

Players continue to alternate turns completing all nine rounds of play.

Once the game is complete, players add up all "nine holes". The player with the least accumulative score is the winner.

VARIATION:

Try division and play as follows.

Player rolls:  and flips:

$$4 \overline{)30}^{\,7R2}$$

Players take the quotient and remainder and add them together for their score for the hole (e.g. 7 + 2 = 9).

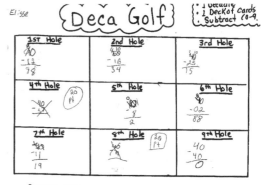

Elisse

{Deca Golf}

• 1 Decadie
• 1 Deck of cards
• Subtract (0-9.

1st Hole	2nd Hole	3rd Hole
90 −12 78	50 −16 34	40 −25 15
4th Hole (20 pt)	5th Hole	6th Hole
40 −5X	10 −8 2	90 −02 88
7th Hole	8th Hole (20 pt)	9th Hole
30 −11 19	46 −7	40 −40 0

SCORE PAD

	1st	2nd	3rd	4th	5th	6th	7th	8th	9th	TOTAL SCORE
Elisse	78	34	15	20	2	88	19	20	0	276
Caroline	7	20	29	10	7	41	80	7	16	167

Describe Your Game Strategy:

When I roll a ten and picked up an 8 I would put it in the ones place because if I put it in the tens place It would be a penalty + and get 20 points, but if I put it in the ones place my score would be 2. Gr 5 Edmonton

Describe Your Game Strategy:

When I rolled a number that was close under my 'target', I put it in the ten's place, but if it was not close enough, I put it in the ones place.

Brianna gr5 Edmonton

HIDE AND SEEK

LEVEL: Grade 3 - 7

PLAYERS: 2 - 4

SKILLS: Basic multiplication facts, missing factors, predicting

EQUIPMENT: Cards King - 9 (King = 0, Ace = 1), one decadie.

GETTING STARTED: Players are dealt six cards each and arrange them face down as follows:

Player One   **Player Two**

Set 1 Set 2 Set 3   Set 1 Set 2 Set 3

Players then select and turn over one card in each set:

Player One   **Player Two**

Set 1 Set 2 Set 3   Set 1 Set 2 Set 3

The decadie is now rolled:

Players now predict and select which pair of cards that when multiplied will be closest to, but not greater than the number rolled.

Player One chooses Set 2 and flips over the hidden card which is a 7. Player One multiplies 8 x 7 = 56. Fifty six is 14 away from the target of 70.

Player Two chooses Set 2 and flips over the hidden card which is a 4. Player Two multiplies 7 x 4 = 28. Twenty eight is 42 away from the target of 70.

Player One earns 1 point for being closest to the target. A new target is rolled and play continues with the remaining two sets of cards. When all three sets have been used, six new cards are dealt and play continues.

VARIATION: Use cards Ace - Queen (Ace = 1, Jack = 11, Queen = 12). Play begins with nine cards face down in three sets of three. Players flip over two cards in each set. The two face up cards are added and will then be multiplied by the hidden third card.

EXAMPLE:

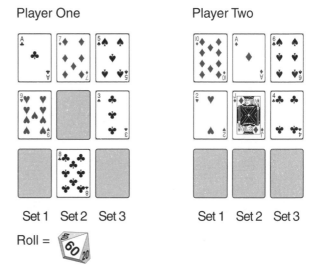

Player One selects Set 3, flips over a 6 and calculates (5 + 3) x 6 = 48. Forty eight is 12 away from the target of 60.

Player Two selects Set 2, flips over a 7 and calculates (11 + 1) x 7 = 84. Eighty four is over the target of 60.

Player One earns 1 point.

MILLENNIUM DICE

(submitted by Marie Sternberg - class of 2000 Grade 5, England)

LEVEL: Grade 4 - 6

SKILLS: Subtracting large numbers, calendar skills, number bonds to 100

PLAYERS: 2 - 4

EQUIPMENT: Two ten-sided (0-9) dice, one decadie, bingo chips

GETTING STARTED: Players alternate rolling the three dice. The two ten-sided dice are added to get the century, and the decadie provides the decade. Players now subtract this number from the current year or the year 2000. The next player rolls, and gets a year in the same manner, and performs the subtraction. The player with the greatest difference earns 1 point.

EXAMPLE: Player One rolls

$5 + 9 = 14$ and 60 is the decade (1 460).

$2\ 000 - 1\ 460 = 540$

Player Two rolls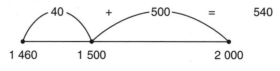

$2 + 8 = 10$ and 40 is the decade (1 040).

$2\ 000 - 1\ 040 = 960$

Player Two earns 1 point, since 960 is greater than 540.

Play continues until one player earns 20 points.

Encourage students to verbalize the year as "fourteen sixty" to understand the "shorthand way" we refer to such centuries.

VARIATION: Use a twenty-sided die to provide the century instead of two ten-sided dice.

TEACHING TIP: Use this game to practice the "adding on" strategy for subtracting:

e.g. $2\ 000 - 1\ 460$

$$40 + 500 = 540$$

1 460   1 500   2 000

ROLL OF THE CENTURY

(submitted by Marie Sternberg - class of 2000 Grade 5, England)

LEVEL: Grade 4 - 6

SKILLS: Multiplying by tens, rounding, comparing to the closest hundred, multiple addend addition

PLAYERS: 2

EQUIPMENT: One ten-sided (0-9) die, one decadie

GETTING STARTED: Players alternate rolling both dice and multiplying the two numbers together. The player with the product closest to any hundred number earns the points for that round.

EXAMPLE:

Player One

Player Two

6 x 40 = 240   8 x 90 = 720

Player Two earns 20 points, as 720 is closer to 700 than 240 is to 200.

The points a player earns is determined by the "decade difference" from the closest hundred number. For example, 340 would earn a player 40 points if that player's number was closest to a hundred number; 170 would earn 30 points (closest to 200), etc.

If numbers are equally close to the nearest hundred, (i.e. players "tie") no one earns points. If a player gets a multiple of 100 (or 0) they automatically earn 100 points!

Players keep a running tally of their own points. The first player to reach or exceed 500 points is the winner.

THOUGHT PROVOKERS:

1. On average, how many rolls do you think it will take for one player to reach 500?

2. If the rules were written so the player with the product furthest from any hundred number earns the points, would the game go quicker? Why or why not?

Connor

ROLL OF THE CENTURY

Roll 1 Decade + 1 10-sided

Rules: Roll both dice and multiply.
Player with the product closest to any hundred number earns the points.
The "decade difference" from the closest hundred number = point.

ACCUMULATIVE TOTAL	WORKING AREA
100	$80 \times 2 = 160$ (tie)
+ 100	$80 \times 4 = 320$ (tie)
200	$40 \times 6 = 240$
100	$90 \times 3 = 270$
300	$80 \times 2 = 160$
100	$70 \times 5 = 350$
400	$70 \times 6 = 420$
100	$40 \times 9 = 360$
(500)	$00 \times 7 = 0$ (tie)
	$30 \times 0 = 0$ *
	$80 \times 5 = 400$ *
	$70 \times 0 = 0$ *
	$60 \times 0 = 0$ *
	$80 \times 7 = 560$
	$40 \times 7 = 280$ (tie)
	$60 \times 9 = 540$ (tie)
	$20 \times 7 = 140$
	$70 \times 0 = 0$ *

18 rolls!

Connor rules the Century!!

1. On average how many rolls to reach 500? This time it was (18) but I'd have to play again to compare.

2. If we changed the point diff. rule, would the game go quicker? I think it would be the same because it would affect both players the same way.

RED RACERS

LEVEL: Grade 4 - 8

SKILLS: Multiplying by multiples of 10, probability

PLAYERS: 2

EQUIPMENT: One ten-sided (0-9) die, one decadie, one gameboard per player (see reproducibles), pencil

GETTING STARTED: **Qualifying Laps**

Players alternate rolling both dice, multiplying the two numbers, and writing the product on their chart. After 10 rolls or laps, players will exchange gameboards.

Elimination Laps

Players alternate rolling both dice, ten times each, this time eliminating their opponent's numbers (if they occur) in that lap. If a player rolls a number that occurs more than once, both of these numbers would be eliminated at the same time. In the example below, Player Two has two 80's and would eliminate both. The player who has the most numbers remaining wins the heat and earns 1 point. Play continues until one player earns 5 points.

EXAMPLE: **Qualifying Laps**

Player One rolls a 1 and an 80 and fills in 80 on their chart (1 x 80 = 80).

Player Two rolls a 4 and a 60 and fills in 240 on their chart (4 x 60 = 240).

After ten laps, players' charts might look something like this:

Player One	Player Two
80	240
100	80
420	360
0	80
180	160
0	160
160	360
560	400
160	100
30	420

VARIATION I: Use two ten-sided dice and add to 18.

EXAMPLE: Each player rolls ten sums for qualifying.

6 + 8 = 14
7 + 5 = 12, etc.

Then players exchange boards to try eliminating each others sums.

TEACHING TIP: You may want students to record the complete math sentence (e.g. 6 x 60 = 360).

Elimination Laps

240
~~80~~
360
~~80~~
160
160
360
400
100
420

Players now exchange gameboards and attempt to eliminate their opponent's numbers.

Player One rolls a 2 and a 40 and crosses out both 80's on Player Two's gameboard (2 x 40 = 80).

If Player Two's gameboard had eight numbers remaining and Player One's gameboard had only six numbers remaining after ten laps, then Player Two wins the heat and earns 1 point.

VARIATION II:	Try playing using a twenty-sided or thirty-sided die instead of one ten-sided die, or two ten-sided dice to practice the 9 x 9 multiplication table.

Mackenzie C

I Think this game is a keeper because it really helped me practise multiplying by ten and it was fun trying to eliminate Courtneys numbers. We even tried playing it with two 10 sided dice to practise our regular multiplication facts to 81. I was a lot of fun too! (Even though she beat me!) 😊

THOUGHT PROVOKERS:

Which numbers are easiest to eliminate? Why?

1. What are all the numbers on:

   a) a ten-sided die?

   b) a decadie?

2. What are all the possible products you can get from rolling the above two dice and multiplying the numbers together? Try to think of a system for organizing your answer.

MULTIPLICATION OUTCOME CHART FOR RED RACERS

X	0	1	2	3	4	5	6	7	8	9
00	0	0	0	0	0	0	0	0	0	0
10	0	10	20	30	40	50	60	70	80	90
20	0	20	40	60	80	100	120	140	160	180
30	0	30	60	90	120	150	180	210	240	270
40	0	40	80	120	160	200	240	280	320	360
50	0	50	100	150	200	250	300	350	400	450
60	0	60	120	180	240	300	360	420	480	540
70	0	70	140	210	280	350	420	490	560	630
80	0	80	160	240	320	400	480	560	640	720
90	0	90	180	270	360	450	540	630	720	810

Players are rolling one decdadie and one ten-sided (0-9) die.

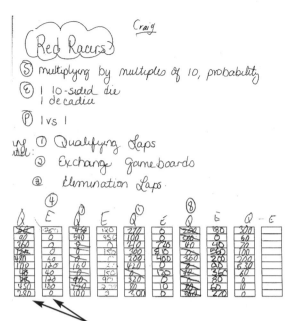

NOTE: These students exchanged sheets to do the eliminating and recorded all elimination rolls. The circled numbers above the products indicate how many numbers they were able to eliminate in 10 rolls. Class data is shown.

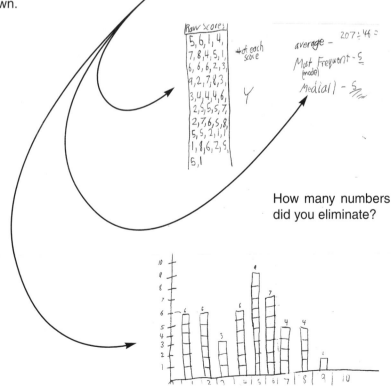

How many numbers did you eliminate?

159

Blaire

Red Racers

Qualifying Round	Rolls	Describe The Game!
~~360~~	✓	$\frac{6}{10}$ 60%
~~320~~	✓	
~~30~~	✓	I Won because I rolled
~~40~~	✓	better numbers and
~~10~~	✓	also because some
720	✓	numbers are harder to
~~80~~	✓	cross off like 10, 320,
10	✓	720 and 540. Some of
~~210~~	✓	the easy number are
~~180~~	✓	0, 360, 240

Qualifying Round	Rolls	Describe The Game!!
~~60~~	✓	$\frac{8}{10}$ 80%
~~150~~	✓	
~~80~~	✓	I was easy for
540	✓	me because Blaire
~~360~~	✓	had two doubles.
~~300~~	✓	
60	✓	
~~0~~	✓	
~~360~~	✓	
630		

* Equipment : 1 decadie and 1 ten-sided (0-9)
* Rules: Roll both dice, multiply and record products (ten times)

FOOTBALL FACTOR

LEVEL: Grade 4 - 8

SKILLS: Multiplying 10's and 1's, multiple addend addition, probability

PLAYERS: 2

EQUIPMENT: One decadie, gameboard (see reproducibles), pencil

GETTING STARTED: The goal of the game is to have the greatest number of points after four quarters. Players start off by choosing a "touch down factor". This value will be multiplied by the dice roll to determine the points earned for a touch down.

TEACHING TIP: Encourage students to select the times tables that they need to practice the most (e.g. 6 x, 7 x, 8 x, 12 x).

Player One starts by rolling the decadie and multiplying the die by the touch down factor to determine their touch down score. Player One then rolls a second decadie. This value is the field goal score. It is added to the touch down score to determine the total score for the first quarter.

The next player takes their turn and play continues until both players have played four quarters.

Players can record their scores in the Football Factor gameboard.

EXAMPLE: Teams choose 6 to be the touch down factor.

Player One, First Quarter

Touch Down Roll:

Touch Down Score = 6 x 90 = 540

Field Goal Roll:

Field Goal Score = 40

Player One's total score for the first quarter is 580 (540 + 40).

Player Two, First Quarter

Touch Down Roll:

Touch Down Score = 6 x 80 = 480

Field Goal Roll:

Field Goal Score = 90

Player Two's total score for the first quarter is 570 (480 + 90).

Player One

	Touchdown	Field Goal	Total
1st Quarter	6 x 90 = 540	40	540 + 40 = 580
2nd Quarter	6 x 40 = 240	30	240 + 30 = 270
3rd Quarter	6 x 20 = 120	90	120 + 90 = 210
4th Quarter	6 x 70 = 420	00	420 + 00 = 420

Total Football Score | 1480 |

Player Two

	Touchdown	Field Goal	Total
1st Quarter	6 x 80 = 480	90	480 + 90 = 570

Play continues until all four quarters are played out. The player with the greatest accumulated point total is the winner.

Encourage players to change the touch down factor so that they can practice all the times tables - especially 6 x, 7 x, 8 x and 12 x.

THOUGHT PROVOKERS:

Have all the students play the same scoring system and record all totals.

1. What is the average point total when the touch down factor is 6? Once this is determined, predict and test out how this average will change when the touch down factor is 7 or 8, etc.

The following samples show 56 games played out in a class. Scores were arranged to determine median.

NOTE: The median was the same as the average. AMAZING!!

Foot ball Factor   7-3

90, 160, 310, 1080, 1120, 1300, 1340, 1400, 1420,

1440, 1460, 1460, 1470, 1470, 1550, 1550, 1630,

1640, 1640, 1690, 1700, 1730, 1760, 1850,

1890, 1890, 1900, $\boxed{1930}$, 1940, 1950, 1960,

1960, 1990, 2100, 2150, 2160, 2160, 2170,

2190, 2200, 2340, 2350, 2380, 2430,

2480, 2480, 2600, 2670, 2700, 2750,

2840, 2860, 2890, 2990, 3190, 3300 ?

NOTE: Class scores arranged in order to determine median. The class was amazed to see how closely it matched the mean (average).

56 games
Range 90 - 3300
Average - 1929.46
28 game 1930.

Total 108 050

max score per quarter (90×8) +90 = 810
per game 810×4 = 3240.

I think football factor is a really kool game because it was really easy to play and it was neat that we got our average on the 28ᵗʰ game.

Melissa Sutherland

163

I think football faction is a great game
for learning your multiplication and addition
skills. I thought that it was interesting
that we got our average by the 25 game that
we played.

Felisha
Corbeil
7-3
Nov 15/00

Zach Kipp 7-3

Football factor was fun because I knew
multiplycation and it was very easy for me.
The night, last night I played with my brother
and said it was fun because he knew multiply
and it was good practice for him.

Garret Hunnah 7-3

Football factors was fun because my favorite
sport is football and its fun to play games instead
of do work

Loved football factors.
You always have something
todo. You can do you're partners
in you're head. It helped me
with my math alot.

Mikayla Kesseler   7-3
                          Nov. 15/00
Football Factor   Paula V.
I thought Football Factor was a fun
game because I like to multiply and it
pushed me to work fast and memorize
the 8's.

Football Factor 8-2

160, 500, 520, 640, 1020, 1110, 1170, 1330, 1360, 1370, 1440,

1460, 1480, 1510, 1540, 1600, 1610, 1670, 1740, 1810.

1900, 1910, 1930, 1930 2010, 2030, 2050, 2060

2060, 2060, 2070, 2130, 2160, 2170, 2210, 2220, 2280

2310, 2470, 2480, 2500, 2530, 2530, 2540, 2580

2640, 2650, 2860, 2980

50 games
Range 160-2980
Average - 1825.80
Total score 91290
25th game - 1930.

164

Math Homework

name Craig Mayers gr 6
date November N

Brain Booster: What is the possible football score with a factor of 6? Can you figure out all scores for factors 0-12?

$6 \rightarrow$
$\begin{array}{r} 90 \times 6 \\ 540 \\ + 90 \\ \hline 630 \end{array}$
$\begin{array}{r} '680 \\ 630 \\ 630 \\ 630 \\ \hline (2520) \end{array}$

0-90

$\begin{array}{r} 90 \\ \times 180 \\ \hline (180) \end{array}$
$\begin{array}{r} 2700 \\ 90 \\ \hline (360) \end{array}$
$\begin{array}{r} 360 \\ 90 \\ \hline (450) \end{array}$
$\begin{array}{r} 450 \\ 90 \\ \hline (640) \end{array}$
$\begin{array}{r} 630 \\ 90 \\ \hline (2.70) \end{array}$
$\begin{array}{r} 720 \\ 90 \\ \hline (810) \end{array}$
$\begin{array}{r} 900 \\ 90 \\ \hline (990) \end{array}$
$\begin{array}{r} '9901 \\ 1080 \end{array}$
$\begin{array}{r} 1080 \\ 90 \\ \hline 1170 \end{array}$

Answers

0-90×4=360
1-150×4=600
2-270+4=1080
3-360×4=1440
4-450×4=1800
5-540×4=2160
6-630×4=2520
7-720×4=2880
8-810×4=3240
9-900×4=3600
10-990×4=3960
11-1080×4=4320
12-1170×4=4680

$\begin{array}{r} ^2150 \\ \times 4 \\ \hline 600 \end{array}$

$\begin{array}{r} ^2270 \\ \times 4 \\ \hline 1080 \end{array}$
$\begin{array}{r} ^2450 \\ \times 4 \\ \hline 1800 \end{array}$
$\begin{array}{r} ^236 0 \\ \times 4 \\ \hline 1440 \end{array}$

$\begin{array}{r} 720 \\ \times 4 \\ \hline 2880 \end{array}$
$\begin{array}{r} 810 \\ \times 4 \\ \hline 3240 \end{array}$
$\begin{array}{r} 900 \\ \times 4 \\ \hline 3600 \end{array}$

$\begin{array}{r} 1170 \\ \times 4 \\ \hline 4680 \end{array}$
$\begin{array}{r} ^31080 \\ \times 4 \\ \hline 4320 \end{array}$
$\begin{array}{r} 990 \\ \times 4 \\ \hline 3960 \end{array}$

$\begin{array}{r} ^1540 \\ \times 4 \\ \hline 2160 \end{array}$

165

THE GREAT DIVIDE

LEVEL: Grade 3 - 6

SKILLS: Dividing and adding accumulative sums

PLAYERS: 2

EQUIPMENT: One decadie, one regular die, gameboard (see reproducibles), paper, pencil

GETTING STARTED: Player One rolls the decadie and regular die. Player One now attempts to divide the number rolled on the regular die into the number rolled on the decadie. If it can be divided evenly, that player earns points equal to the quotient and records this on paper.

If the number cannot be divided without remainders, then that player earns no points. Players continue rolling and taking turns until one player reaches an accumulative sum of 200.

EXAMPLE:

Player One	Points	Accumulated Total
Roll 1		
$70 \div 5 = 14$	14	14
Roll 2		
$50 \div 2 = 25$	25	39 (14 + 25)
Roll 3		
$30 \div 2 = 15$	15	54 (39 + 15)

Player Two	Points	Accumulated Total
Roll 1		
$40 \div 3 = 13$ R1	0	0
Roll 2		
$30 \div 6 = 5$	5	5 (0 + 5)
Roll 3		
$60 \div 3 = 20$	20	25 (5 + 20)

VARIATION:

Have players roll 1 decadie and one ten-sided (0-9) die (e.g. 90 ÷ 9 = 10).

The Great Divide

You Need: 1 Decadie / 1 Regular die / Paper, pencil / 2 Players

ROLL:	POINTS:	ACCUMULATIVE Total:
90 ÷ 4 = 22 R2	0	0
50 ÷ 5 = 10	10	10
20 ÷ 2 = 10	10	20
90 ÷ 5 = 18	18	38
5 ÷ 0 = 0	0	38
40 ÷ 2 = 20	20	58
70 ÷ 1 = 70	70	128
60 ÷ 2 = 30	30	158
20 ÷ 4 = 5	5	163
70 ÷ 5 = 14	14	177
90 ÷ 2 = 45	45	222 We went past 200!
0 ÷ 2 = 0	0	222
90 ÷ 5 = 18	18	240
80 ÷ 6 = 13 R2	0	240
90 ÷ 3 = 30	30	270

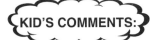

KID'S COMMENTS:

This game is great for reviewing division facts and using "mental math strategies" to figure out the answer without using a calculator. For example, if you don't know the answer for 90 ÷ 5, think, "What is half of 90?" The answer would be 45. Now think, "What is 45 ÷ 5?" The answer is 9. So now double that to get your answer (9 x 2 = 18)! I call this the "NO CALCULATOR CHALLENGE"!

QUOTIENT WAR

LEVEL: Grade 3 - 6

SKILLS: Division with remainders

PLAYERS: 2 - 4

EQUIPMENT: One decadie and one regular die per player, calculator (optional)

GETTING STARTED: Each player rolls their two dice and divides them. The player with the least quotient earns 1 point.

EXAMPLE: Player One rolls: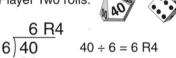

$$\begin{array}{r} 30 \\ 2\overline{)60} \end{array} \qquad 60 \div 2 = 30$$

Player Two rolls:

$$\begin{array}{r} 6 \text{ R4} \\ 6\overline{)40} \\ \underline{36} \\ 4 \end{array} \qquad 40 \div 6 = 6 \text{ R4}$$

Player Two verbalizes, "6 R4 is a smaller quotient than 30." and earns 1 point. In the event of a tie (i.e. both players have the same quotient) both players earn 1 point. Play continues for a set period of time. Players always re-roll when 00 is rolled. The player with the most points wins.

TEACHING TIP: Have players record each math sentence in their games book and keep a running total of their accumulated points. Players are encouraged to use their calculators only when checking for accuracy.

DIVISION DECISION

LEVEL: Grade 3 - 7

SKILLS: Division with remainders

PLAYERS: 2

EQUIPMENT: Hundred Board (see reproducibles), bingo chips or other markers, one decadie, one ten-sided (0-9) die or regular die, calculator (optional when checking for accuracy).

GETTING STARTED: The goal of the game is to be the first player to reach 100 on the hundred board. Players both begin by placing their marker on number 1. Player One begins by rolling the decadie and ten-sided die. The player now divides the numbers and figures out the remainder.

$$7{\overline{\smash{)}\,80}} \quad 11\,R3$$

Player One moves ahead on the hundred board the number of spaces equal to the remainder. In this case, Player One moves ahead three spaces to 4. Player Two now takes their turn rolling the dice, dividing the numbers and finding the remainder. If a player rolls a 0 or 00, they must re-roll. If a player divides the numbers and there is no remainder (e.g. $60 \div 6 = 10$ with 0 as the remainder) then that player does not move forward on their board. Players continue to alternate turns and move along the hundreds board. The first player to reach 100 wins.

THOUGHT PROVOKERS:

1. Which combination of numbers give you the highest remainders?

2. Which combination of numbers give you the least or no remainders?

FACTOR BUZZ

LEVEL: Grade 4 - 7

SKILLS: Finding factors, mental math, adding four addends, multiplication and division

PLAYERS: 2 - 4 or teams of 2 vs. 2 (equal skill level)

EQUIPMENT: Four decadice, paper, pencil, calculator (optional to check for accuracy)

GETTING STARTED: The goal of the game is to be the first player to verbalize at least five factors of the target number. To begin, one player rolls all four dice to establish the number that all players will use in the round. Each player mentally adds up the dice to reach that number. Players now race to record at least five different factors for this number. Players may not record the target number and the number 1 as possible factors. The first player to record at least five factors says, "Buzz". If all factors are correct, then that player earns 1 point.

EXAMPLE: Four dice rolled:

Target Number = 210 (30 + 60 + 80 + 40)

Players record their factors and Player Two says "Buzz" first. Player Two reads their factors:

30, 7, 5, 105 and 2

All are correct factors so Player Two earns 1 point.

Other correct factors would be 10, 21, 70 and 3.

 **TEACHING TIPS:**
1. Over time, players will realize that all targets will have the following factors: 2 (and its other related factor), 5 and 10 (and its other related factor). Once players are at this level, play Bonus Buzz variation.

2. Players may want to analyze the numbers rolled on the dice to establish a starting point for determining some or any possible factors.

THOUGHT PROVOKERS:

1. We think there will always be a minimum of five factors. Do you agree?

2. Which number(s) have the most factors?

3. Which number(s) have the least?

4. Will most of the target numbers be over 100? Why?

VARIATION:

Bonus Buzz

Players may earn an additional point for any factor over and above 2 (and it's other factor), 5 and 10 (and its other factor). See question #8 in the following sample.

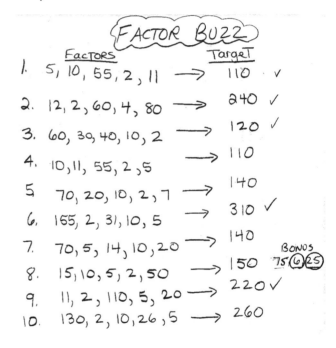

FACTOR BUZZ

	FacTORS	TargeT	
1.	5, 10, 55, 2, 11 ⟶	110	✓
2.	12, 2, 60, 4, 80 ⟶	240	✓
3.	60, 30, 40, 10, 2 ⟶	120	✓
4.	10, 11, 55, 2, 5 ⟶	110	
5	70, 20, 10, 2, 7 ⟶	140	
6.	155, 2, 31, 10, 5 ⟶	310	✓
7.	70, 5, 14, 10, 20 ⟶	140	
8.	15, 10, 5, 2, 50 ⟶	150	BONUS 75 6 25
9.	11, 2, 110, 5, 20 ⟶	220	✓
10.	130, 2, 10, 26, 5 ⟶	260	

TEACHING TIP:

Try setting up the game in teams of 2 vs. 2. Have teams work across from each other with a divider in between to "hide" their work from one another during the play.

Factor Buzz

	Factors		Target #
1.	5, 10, 2, 10, 55 $\longrightarrow$		110
2.	3, 12, 60, 4, 8 $\longrightarrow$		240
3.	2, 120~~X~~, 4, 5 $\longmapsto$		120 ×
4.	5, 10, 2, 11, 55 $\rightarrow$		110
5.	2, 70, 5, 10, 14 $\longrightarrow$		140
6.	155, .5, .10, .001, .0001 $\Rightarrow$		310
7.	2, 70, 5, 7, 10 $\longrightarrow$		140
8.	25, 50, 3, 5, 10 $\longrightarrow$		150
9.	20, 2, 5, 10, 11 $\longrightarrow$		220

1
```
  75
  75
 150
```

```
   70
2)140
  14
  0
  0
```

```
    155  R0
2)310
   2
   11
   10
   10
   0
   0
```

10, 2, 5, 55, 2 ← 260

GOT IT / CLOSEST TO!

LEVEL: Grade 4 - 8

SKILLS: Mixed operations (+, -, x, ÷), order of operations, exponents

PLAYERS: Teams of 2 vs. 2, equal skill level

EQUIPMENT: One decadie, two ten-sided (0-9) dice, two regular dice, gameboard (see reproducibles), pencil

GETTING STARTED: All five dice are rolled and set before the two teams. Players are not allowed to touch the dice once they are rolled. The goal of the teams is to target the number on the decadice using the four remaining dice. All remaining dice must be used once.

EXAMPLE:

The dice are rolled:  ← Target Decadie

Dice for targeting → the decadie

Team One says "Got It" as they calculated an exact bullseye: (5 + 5) x (4 - 3) = 10. Team One now records their math.

There will be roll combinations that cannot be calculated to a bullseye. In this case, a team may call "Closest To", verbalize their sentence and record their math.

EXAMPLE:

The dice are rolled: ← Target Decadie

Dice for targeting → the decadie

Team Two says "Closest To".

$8^2 - 1 - 1 = 62$

The team who calls out first and correctly gives an answer earns 5 points unless the other team's equation is closer.

In the event a team calls out first and then gives an incorrect response, their opponents now have the opportunity to give either a "Got It" or "Closest To" response and potentially earn 5 points.

The dice are re-rolled for the next round. Play continues until one team earns 100 points.

 **TEACHING TIP:** This game can be played non-competitively. Each team separately records their own math and then compare their answers. The team closest to the target number would earn the points. If both teams "got it", they would both earn points.

Got it! / Closest To!

You Need :
1 Decadie (TARGET ROLL)
2 10-SIDED (0-9)
2 Regular Dice

AJVAAGE
7-3

	TARGET :	NUMBERS :	EVALUATE :	
1.	90	3,5,4,6	$4^3 + (5 \times 6) = 94$	5
2.	90	4, 6, 6, 2	$(6+6-2) \times 4 = 40$	10
3.	10	2, 3, 5, 2	$2^3 + 5 - 2 = 11$	5
4.	50	5, 4, 3, 2	$3^2 \times 5 + 4 = 49$	5
5.	60	3, 3, 5, 1	$(3+1) \times 5 \times 3 = 60$	
6.	0	7, 4, 1, 8		
7.				

Got it! Closest To!

YOU NEED: 1 Decadie, 2 (0-9) dice, 2 regular dice

Target:	Numbers:	Evaluate:
eg. 90	4, 1, 3, 1	$3^4 + 1 + 1 = 83$
30	6, 4, 8, 1	$6 \times 4 + 8 - 1 = 31$
80	6, 6, 4, 3	$3^4 - (6 \div 6) = 80$ ✩
0	5, 4, 9, 0	$(5 + 4) - (9 + 0) = 0$ ✩
50	9, 2, 6, 1	$9 \times 6 - (2 + 1) = 51$
60	5, 4, 5, 0	
10	6, 4, 4, 7	
70	3, 3, 1, 6	

KID'S COMMENTS: This game helped me analyze different combinations of numbers when trying to reach the target. We also had to review the rules for the order of operations because we forgot how! It makes a difference in getting to the right answer.

COMBO DECADE DUEL

LEVEL: Grade 4 - 7

SKILLS: Mixed operations with 10's (+, -, x, ÷), problem solving, order of operations

PLAYERS: 2 vs. 2

EQUIPMENT: Four decadice, paper, pencil

GETTING STARTED: The goal of the game is for players to bullseye the target sum. Play begins by rolling all four decadice to establish the target sum.

Roll:

Target Sum = 70 + 90 + 0 + 20 = 180

Both teams record the rolls and now attempt to target 180.

To begin the first round, Team One rolls the four decadice and attempts to create an equation from the dice that equals the target. All four operations (+, -, x, ÷) may be used and all or only some of the dice may be used in the equation. Each number may only be used once.

EXAMPLE: Team One rolls:

Target is 180. Team One creates the following equation:

40 x 40 + 10 = 170

Team Two rolls:

Team Two creates the following equation:

90 + 50 + 70 - 30 = 180

Team Two hits the target (equalling 180) and earns 4 points for the round (1 point per die used in the equation).

If neither team reaches (hits) the target, the team closest to the target (teams may be greater than the target) earns 1 point per die used in the combination. The first team to earn 50 points is the winner.

 **TEACHING TIP:** You can set a minimum number of dice to be used in a combination in order to be a scoring combination. Include an operation die for grades 4 - 7 and have it rolled with the target roll. The operation rolled must be used at least once in the combination.

EXAMPLE: Roll:

Target is 180. Team One creates the following equation:

$(40 + 40) \times 60 \div 30 = 160$

You may also wish to allow positive or negative integers and exponents for enrichment.

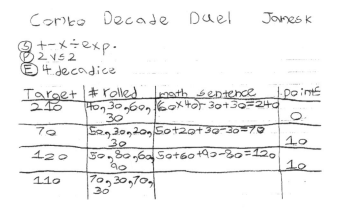

Combo Decade Duel   James k

Ⓢ +−×÷ exp.
Ⓟ 2 vs 2
Ⓔ 4 decadice

Target	# rolled	math sentence	points
210	40, 30, 60, 30	(60×40)−30+30=240	0
70	50, 30, 20, 30	50+20+30−30=70	10
120	50, 80, 60, 90	50+60+90−80=120	10
110	70, 30, 70, 30		

COMBO SNAP

LEVEL: Grade 5 and up

SKILLS: Mixed operations (+, -, x, ÷), problem solving

PLAYERS: 2 or more

EQUIPMENT: One decadie, cards Ace - King (Ace = 1, Jack = 11, Queen = 12, King = 0)

GETTING STARTED: All players build a five by five card grid with twenty-five random cards, face up. The goal of the game is for each player to remove all the cards from their grid. To begin, one player rolls the decadie for all players to use. Players now look for any five card combination that equals the target number rolled (all operations may be used). The first player to pick up a combination says "Combo Snap" and all other players must stop. The player who called out, now verbalizes their five card combination math sentence (e.g. if the decadie equals 50, players might take the following cards to create: 5 x 9 - 4 + 11 - 2 = 50). If they successfully targeted the die, that player now places their five cards aside to begin their point pile. If that player makes an error and their combination does not equal the target number, those cards are replaced into their grid and the other players now resume the play. The player who made an error is disqualified until a new number is rolled. When a combination has successfully been removed from one player's grid, a new number is rolled on the decadie. Play continues until one player removes their last five cards.

 TEACHING TIP: Players may want to pay close attention to the numbers on the cards they leave behind. Your last five cards are crucial to the success of the game. For instance, if you are left with the following cards and the target rolled equals a high number, it would be very difficult to equal the target.

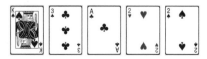

TARGET ZERO

(submitted by Marie Sternberg - class of 2000 Grade 5, England)

LEVEL: Grade 4 - 9

SKILLS: Adding and subtracting 10's, working with negative numbers

PLAYERS: 2 or solitaire

EQUIPMENT: One decadie, one number line per player (see reproducibles), pencil

GETTING STARTED: Both players start at 100. Player One rolls the decadie and subtracts this number from 100. Player Two rolls the die, subtracts their number from 100. The object of the game is reach zero by an exact roll. Players may add or subtract their roll to do so. The first player to reach zero earns 1 point.

EXAMPLE: The following is an example of Player One's rolls only:

First roll: 100 - 20 = 80

Second roll: 80 - 60 = 20

Third roll: 20 - 30 = -10

Fourth roll: -10 + 90 = 80

Fifth roll: 80 - 80 = 0

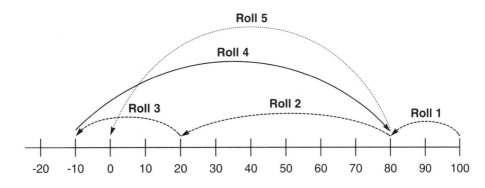

VARIATION: Using a ten sided (0-9) die, players add or subtract from 100 to reach 0.

THOUGHT PROVOKERS:

1. What is the least number of rolls required to reach zero? Why?

2. What is the average number of rolls required to reach zero (compare with other samples)?

3. Which number of rolls occurs most often? Why?

TARGET ZERO   Riki

ROLL:	My Math Sentence:
#1 (60)	100-60 = 40
#2 (30)	40-30 = 10
#3 (50)	10-50 = -40
#4 (30)	-40+30 = -10
#5 (00)	10+00 = 10
#6 (00)	10+00 = 10
#7 (80)	10+80 = 90
#8 (40)	90-40 = 50 It took 9 rolls !
#9 (50)	50-50 = 0
#1 (10)	100-10 = 90
#2 (70)	90-70 = 20
#3 (60)	20-60 = -40
#4 (00)	-40+00 = -40
#5 (30)	-40+30 = -10
#6 (00)	-10+00 = -10
#7 (70)	-10+70 = 60
#8 (10)	60-10 = 50
#9 (00)	50+00 = 50

TEACHING TIP: Have players <u>predict</u> how many rolls they think it will take to target zero before they begin to play.

180

DECI-DECA

LEVEL:	Grade 6 - 9
SKILLS:	Mental math, multiplying decimals and whole numbers
PLAYERS:	2
EQUIPMENT:	Cards King - 9 (King = 0, Ace = 1), calculators, gameboards: A, B, or C (see reproducibles)
GETTING STARTED:	The goal of the game is to create the greatest product. Before the game begins, players need to choose the same gameboard from which to play (each player needs their own board). Both players now flip a card off the top of their deck, place it into their gameboard and roll their decadie. Each player now mentally calculates their product by multiplying the cards as a decimal and the decadie as the whole number.
EXAMPLE:	Player One

Player Two

Player Two verbalizes "32 is greater than 6" and earns Player One's card (and places it into their point pile). If a player verbalizes their product correctly without using a calculator, then they may take a <u>bonus</u> card off their card pile and place it into their point pile.

Play continues for a set period of time. The player with the most cards wins.

KIDS COMMENTS:

"This game helped me practice my mental math. In order to calculate the product, I multiplied and <u>adjusted</u> the decimal."

fractions
and
$ money$

$\frac{1}{4} \times \frac{1}{2}$

0.25

ELIZABETH 1996

one penny
1993

Mackenzie
Mcurrah

$10
TEN

5
$FIVE DOLLARS

Fractions, Money & More

DIEING FOR FRACTIONS

LEVEL:	Grade 4 - 6
SKILLS:	Building and comparing proper fractions, reducing to simplest form and comparing
PLAYERS:	Teams of 2 vs. 2
EQUIPMENT:	Two decadice per player, pencil, paper
GETTING STARTED:	To begin, both players roll their two dice. Players arrange their dice to create a proper fraction and then reduce this fraction to its simplest terms. If a player rolls a 00 on a die, they must re-roll. Players then compare their fractions and the player who rolls the greater fraction earns 1 point. If players tie, then both players earn 2 points.
EXAMPLE:	Player One rolls:

Player One now creates and simplifies their fraction:

$$\frac{20}{40} = \frac{1}{2}$$

Player Two rolls:

Player Two re-rolls the 00 die:

Player Two now creates and simplifies their fraction:

$$\frac{40}{90} = \frac{4}{9}$$

Player One now verbalizes, "One-half is greater than four-ninths" and earns 1 point. If necessary, players may use fraction pieces to "build" their fractions and then compare.

DIEING FOR FRACTIONS CHALLENGER

LEVEL: Grade 5 - 8

SKILLS: Adding proper fractions, finding common denominators, comparing fractions

PLAYERS: Teams of 2 vs. 2

EQUIPMENT: Four decadice, paper, pencil, fraction pieces (optional)

GETTING STARTED: To begin, Player One rolls all four decadice and arranges the numbers on the dice to build two proper fractions. The goal of the game is to rearrange the dice so that the sum of both fractions is as close to one whole as possible. The player who builds the fraction sum closest to one, earns the point. Players always re-roll when 00 is rolled. If the two fractions built equal one whole exactly, then that player earns 1 bonus point.

EXAMPLE: Player One Rolls:

Player One arranges the dice as follows and records the following fractions:

$$\frac{20}{30} + \frac{10}{60} = \frac{2}{3} + \frac{1}{6} = \frac{4}{6} + \frac{1}{6} = \frac{5}{6}$$

Player One verbalizes, "I have five sixths."

Player Two now takes their turn and rolls:

Player Two arranges the dice as follows and records the following fractions:

$$\frac{10}{30} + \frac{40}{90} = \frac{1}{3} + \frac{4}{9} = \frac{3}{9} + \frac{4}{9} = \frac{7}{9}$$

Player Two now verbalizes, "I have seven-ninths."

Player One now verbalizes, "Five-sixths is greater than seven-ninths" and earns 1 point.

186

GET IN LINE

LEVEL: Grade 4 - 6

SKILLS: Comparing proper fractions

PLAYERS: Teams of 2 vs. 2

EQUIPMENT: Decadice, paper, pencil

GETTING STARTED: The goal of the game is to order five proper fractions from least to greatest. To begin, Player One rolls two decadice and builds a proper fraction. Player One now rolls four more proper fractions for a total of five. Player One must now line up all five fractions from least to greatest in order to earn a point. Players always re-roll when 00 is rolled.

EXAMPLE: Fractions created from Player One's rolls:

$$\frac{20}{50} \quad \frac{30}{70} \quad \frac{10}{40} \quad \frac{70}{80} \quad \frac{60}{90}$$

Player One now reduces their fractions and re-arranges them from least to greatest:

Least to Greatest:

$$\frac{10}{40} \quad \frac{30}{70} \quad \frac{20}{30} \quad \frac{60}{90} \quad \frac{70}{80}$$

Now Reduced:

$$\frac{1}{4} \quad \frac{3}{7} \quad \frac{2}{3} \quad \frac{2}{3} \quad \frac{7}{8}$$

If the player is successful, they earn 1 point. If not, Player Two can attempt to line them up to earn the points. Players continue alternating turns until one player earns 10 points.

TEACHING TIP: Have fraction pieces available so that players may check their answers. Have them record their "line-ups".

VARIATION: Speedy Fractions 2 vs. 2.

Players work as a team. The decadice are rolled five times. The first team to record the fractions, in the proper order and simplify them, earns 1 point.

COUNTING IN CIRCLES

LEVEL: Kindergarten - Grade 2

SKILLS: Counting dimes
Variation: counting dimes and nickels

PLAYERS: Groups of 4 - 6 sitting in a circle

EQUIPMENT: One decadie, play money, ten dimes per player

GETTING STARTED: The goal of the game is to be the player to put down the last dime to equal the target on the decadie. Play starts with one person rolling the decadie to establish the target number for the round.

EXAMPLE: The target is rolled:

Play begins by the player to the left of the roller putting in a dime and verbalizing, "ten cents." The next player to the left adds a dime to the centre and says the accumulated total out loud, "twenty cents." Each player in order puts in their dime until it reaches the established target. The player who puts in the last coin to reach the target (70¢ in the above example) takes all the coins. The player to the immediate left rolls a new target with the decadie, and begins a new round of play by putting in the first dime and so on. Players always re-roll when 00 has been rolled.

VARIATION: Use nickels or a combination of nickels and dimes.

TEACHING TIP: For Kindergarten and grade one students have them use the decadie number line (see reproducibles) as a visual cue. This will help them track the pattern of plus ten (+10) as they add their dimes.

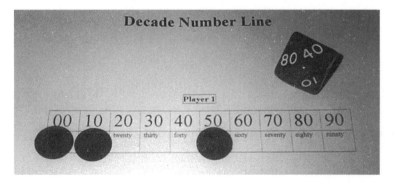

CAPTURE THE CENTER

LEVEL: 3 - 6

SKILLS: Counting mixed change

PLAYERS: Groups of 4 - 6 sitting in a circle

EQUIPMENT: Mixed coins (pennies, nickels, dimes, quarters), one decadie

GETTING STARTED: The goal of the game is to be the player to put down the last coin to equal the target number rolled on the die.

Play starts by one player rolling the decadie to establish the target number for the round. The player to the left of the roller begins by selecting any coin, verbalizing its value, and placing it into the center. The next player to the left adds any coin to the center, and verbalizes the accumulated total out loud. Each player in order selects and adds their coin to the accumulating total in the center. Players may not go over the target on the die. Players always re-roll when 00 is rolled.

EXAMPLE: Player One rolls: (target equals 60¢)

		Accumulated Total
Player One places		25¢
Player Two places		25¢ + 5¢ = 30¢
Player Three places		30¢ + 10¢ = 40¢
Player Four places		40¢ + 5¢ = 45¢
Player One places		45¢ + 1¢ = 46¢
Player Two places		46¢ + 10¢ = 56¢

Player Three places 56¢ + 1¢ = 57¢

Player Four places 57¢ + 1¢ = 58¢

Player One places 58¢ + 1¢ = 59¢

Player Two places 59¢ + 1¢ = 60¢
TARGET!

Player Two hits the target and captures all the coins. A new target is now rolled by the player who "captured the center" and the player to their left starts the next round.

190

EXACTING CHANGE

LEVEL: Grade 3 - 6

SKILLS: Counting mixed change

PLAYERS: 2

EQUIPMENT: Mixed coins, one decadie and one regular die per player, pencil

GETTING STARTED: The goal of the game is to be the player who has used the fewest coins in total to equal their target. Play begins by both players rolling their own target number. Each player rolls one decadie and one regular die.

EXAMPLE: Player One rolls: Target = 32¢

Player Two rolls: Target = 63¢

Both players must now make their target with the fewest coins possible.

Player One uses four coins:

25¢ + 5¢ + 1¢ + 1¢ = 32¢

Player Two uses six coins:

25¢ + 25¢ + 10¢ + 1¢ + 1¢ + 1¢ = 63¢

Since Player One used fewer coins, that player now captures all of the coins and places them in a winning pile.

THOUGHT PROVOKERS:

1. How often does the player with the least target number win all of the coins?

2. What numbers were helpful to roll on the decade dice? Why? The regular dice ? Why?

3. Record the "math" during the play of the game (see student sample on the next page).

4. Now analyze your findings for any patterns. Explain what you found.

Exacting Change

Andie
Gr. 3

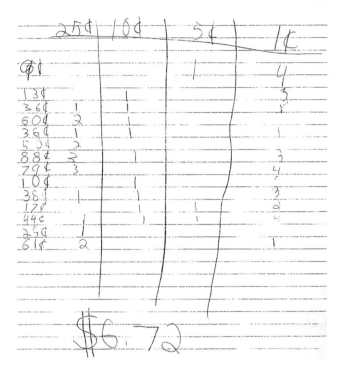

	25¢	10¢	5¢	1¢
$1			1	4
13¢				3
36¢	1	1		
60¢	2			
36¢	1	1		1
5 5¢	3			
88¢	3			3
79¢	3			4
10¢		1		
38¢	1			3
17¢		1		2
44¢	1		1	4
25¢	1			
61¢	2			1

$6.72

192

POCKET SAVINGS

LEVEL:	4 - 8
SKILLS:	Calculating percent (%) discount, counting mixed change
PLAYERS:	2
EQUIPMENT:	Cards King - 9 (King = 0, Ace = 1), mixed coins, paper, pencil, one decadie per player, calculator (optional)
GETTING STARTED:	Play begins by each player building their own price tag with the cards.

EXAMPLE:

Player One
original price

$

Player Two
original price

$

The first card represents the dollar followed by the cents. Each player now rolls their own decadie and calculates that percentage off their price tag. The player who ends up paying the least amount (least price tag after % discount) takes the amount saved in coins and pockets this into their own bank.

EXAMPLE:

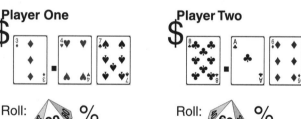

Player One
$

Roll: 20 %

Save 70¢

Cost Now: $2.77

Player Two
$

Roll: 60 %

Save $4.86

Cost Now: $3.30

Player One would pay the least after figuring out the discount and would take 70¢ (their savings) in mixed change and put in into their winnings. A new round begins by making new price tags and rolling the discounts.

The player with the most money after ten rounds of play is the winner.

**TEACHING TIP:**

This is a great activity for teaching mental math strategies for calculating percent/discount and to make real life connections at the same time.

For instance if you were buying something that costs $8.50 that is now 20% off, how do you do it? Well, 10% is $.85 so double that, $1.70 off $8.50. Encourage students to verbalize how they are figuring out their discounts. This is how "shoppers" do it without a calculator in hand when they are in an actual store. Have students do the mental math before going to the calculator for assistance. Have them record and/or verbalize their strategies.

VARIATION:

Play with this "rule" change. The player who rolls the discount that leads to the greatest "savings" would be the winner and would take this amount and place it into their savings. In the above example, Player Two rolled a 60% discount and saved $4.86.

MILLIMETRE MAZE

(submitted by Marie Sternberg - class of 2000 Grade 5, England)

LEVEL: Grade 3 - 8

SKILLS: Using a metric ruler, understanding millimetres, concept of horizontal and vertical, right angles, logical reasoning

PLAYERS: 2

EQUIPMENT: 100 mm x 100 mm grid for each player (see reproducibles) one decadie, pencil, ruler

GETTING STARTED: The object of the game is to get from the top left-hand corner to the bottom right-hand corner by using only straight lines, each line being at a right angle to a previous line and staying within the grid. Player One rolls the decadie, and draws a line the corresponding length in millimetres on the grid starting in the top left. At the end of each line drawn, players pencil a little 'node'. Player Two rolls, and draws a line on their grid, with a node at the end. For subsequent rolls, the line can be drawn from any node players have managed to get on their grids, but it must be at a right angle to an existing line and it must run vertically or horizontally. The player who gets to the bottom right-hand corner first, wins. Players must reach the finish with the exact roll, therefore the best strategy is to set up as many nodes as possible to provide several different routes.

VARIATIONS:

1. Play on a larger gameboard whereby using cm squared paper is essential.

2. Players could alternate turns by sharing one larger grid to race to the finish, using different coloured pencils, and using the same set of lines.

THOUGHT PROVOKERS:

1. Is it better to roll high or low rolls throughout the game or does it make a difference?

2. After playing several rounds did you find you were more successful by having multiple nodes that offered alternate routes (i.e. more options)?

The following diagram illustrates only Player One's rolls:

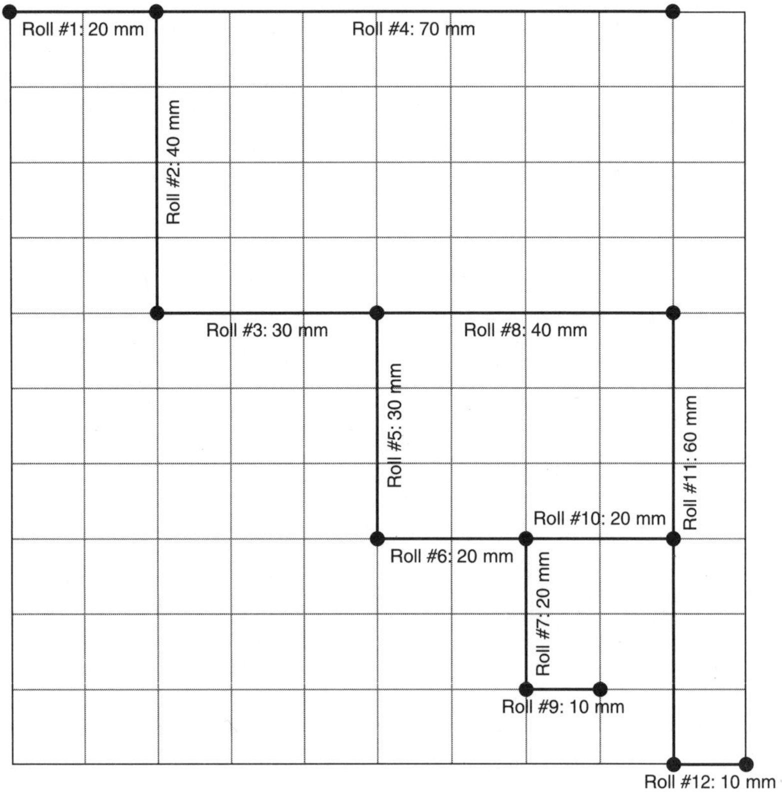

196

Reproducibles

DECA TRAIN

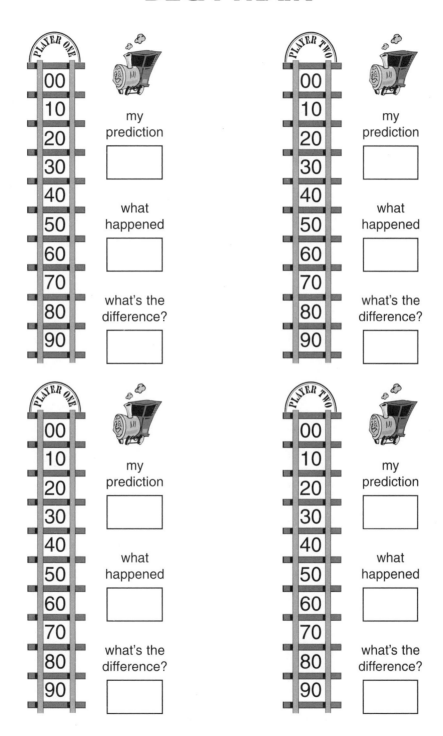

PLAYER ONE

| 00 |
| 10 |
| 20 |
| 30 |
| 40 |
| 50 |
| 60 |
| 70 |
| 80 |
| 90 |

my prediction

what happened

what's the difference?

PLAYER TWO

| 00 |
| 10 |
| 20 |
| 30 |
| 40 |
| 50 |
| 60 |
| 70 |
| 80 |
| 90 |

my prediction

what happened

what's the difference?

PLAYER ONE

| 00 |
| 10 |
| 20 |
| 30 |
| 40 |
| 50 |
| 60 |
| 70 |
| 80 |
| 90 |

my prediction

what happened

what's the difference?

PLAYER TWO

| 00 |
| 10 |
| 20 |
| 30 |
| 40 |
| 50 |
| 60 |
| 70 |
| 80 |
| 90 |

my prediction

what happened

what's the difference?

DECA TRAIN CLASS GRAPH

1 2 3 4 5 6 7 8 9 10 11 12 13 14 15 16 17 18 19 20 21 22 23 24 25 26 27 28 29 30

DECA TRAIN CHALLENGER

My Prediction [ ]
What actually happened [ ]
The difference [ ]

PLAYER ONE

00
10
20
30
40
50
60
70
80
90
100

My Prediction [ ]
What actually happened [ ]
The difference [ ]

PLAYER TWO

00
10
20
30
40
50
60
70
80
90
100

My Prediction [ ]
What actually happened [ ]
The difference [ ]

PLAYER ONE

00
10
20
30
40
50
60
70
80
90
100

My Prediction [ ]
What actually happened [ ]
The difference [ ]

PLAYER TWO

00
10
20
30
40
50
60
70
80
90
100

DECADE NUMBER LINE

Player One

00	10	20	30	40	50	60	70	80	90
zero	ten	twenty	thirty	fourty	fifty	sixty	seventy	eighty	ninety

Player Two

00	10	20	30	40	50	60	70	80	90
zero	ten	twenty	thirty	fourty	fifty	sixty	seventy	eighty	ninety

DECAGRAPHIC

Total Number Of Rolls [   ]

										90
										80
										70
										60
										50
										40
										30
										20
										10
										00

DECAGRAPHIC II

Total Number Of Rolls ☐

										100
										90
										80
										70
										60
										50
										40
										30
										20
										10
										00

DETECTIVE LINE UP

My Score...

I detected...

My Numbers...

SCORING SYSTEM

1. DOUBLES   1 set = _____
         2 sets = _____

2. TRIPLES = _____

3. 4 OF A KIND = _____

4. PLUS 10, 20 OR 30 PATTERN
      with 3 dice = _____
      with 4 dice = _____

5. MULTIPLE PATTERNS = _____

ROLLING A "ROUND"

Total Number of Rolls ☐ Total Rounded Up ☐ Total Rounded Down ☐

										100
										90
										80
										70
										60
										50
										40
										30
										20
										10
										00

HUNDRED BOARD

1	2	3	4	5	6	7	8	9	10
11	12	13	14	15	16	17	18	19	20
21	22	23	24	25	26	27	28	29	30
31	32	33	34	35	36	37	38	39	40
41	42	43	44	45	46	47	48	49	50
51	52	53	54	55	56	57	58	59	60
61	62	63	64	65	66	67	68	69	70
71	72	73	74	75	76	77	78	79	80
81	82	83	84	85	86	87	88	89	90
91	92	93	94	95	96	97	98	99	100

TEN FOR ME

PONDERING PREDICTIONS

Round	Roll 1	Roll 2	Roll 3	Best >	Best <

RANGE GAME GAMEBOARD

00 10 20 30 40 50 60 70 80 90

Round	Target Rolls	Range	Player One	Player Two	Colour Code
1					◯
2					◯
3					◯
4					◯
5					◯
6					◯
7					◯
8					◯
9					◯
10					◯
11					◯
12					◯
13					◯
14					◯
15					◯
16					◯
17					◯
18					◯
19					◯
20					◯

PLAYER ONE'S TOTAL

PLAYER TWO'S TOTAL

RANGE GAME

Grade 4 - 6 Extension

After completing your game, go back through your gameboard and colour in the circles using the following legend:

Next, fill in the totals (out of 20) for each category. Check for accuracy and make sure that your total is 20 /20 (total pieces of data).

COLOUR	CATEGORY	NUMBER OF TIMES OUT OF 20
Yellow	Neither player scored a point (__ __)	/20
Red	Both players scored one point (O O)	/20
Blue	One player scored one point (O __)	/20
Green	One player scored a bullseye (⊙ __)	/20
Orange	Both players scored a bullseye (⊙ ⊙)	/20
Purple	One player scored a bullseye and one player scored one point (⊙ O)	/20

RANGE GAME
GRAPHING ACTIVITY

Transfer your findings to the pie graph using the colour legend. Remember to label your graph to match the categories. Compare your results with at least 3 other groups and explain your findings.

FLIPPIN' OUT

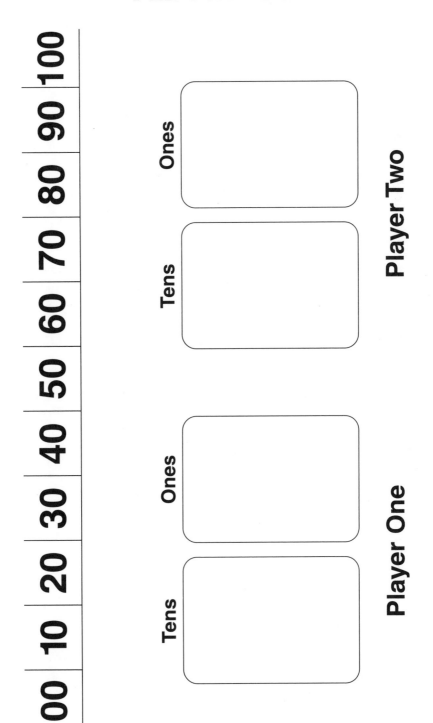

FLIPPIN' OUT VARIATION

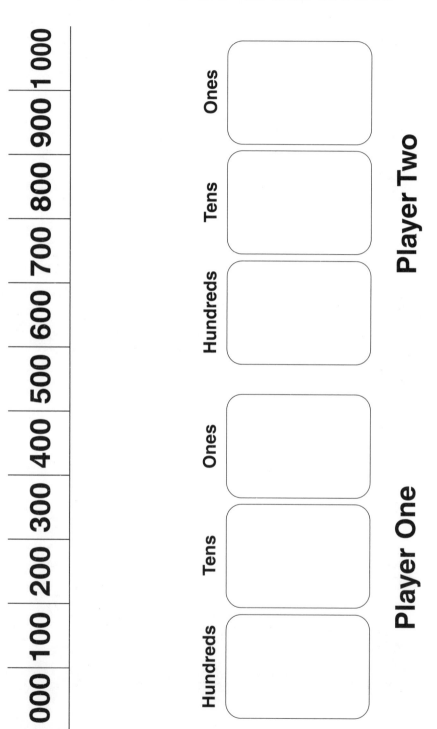

000 | 100 | 200 | 300 | 400 | 500 | 600 | 700 | 800 | 900 | 1 000

Player Two

Ones

Tens

Hundreds

Player One

Ones

Tens

Hundreds

214

A TARGET ROUND

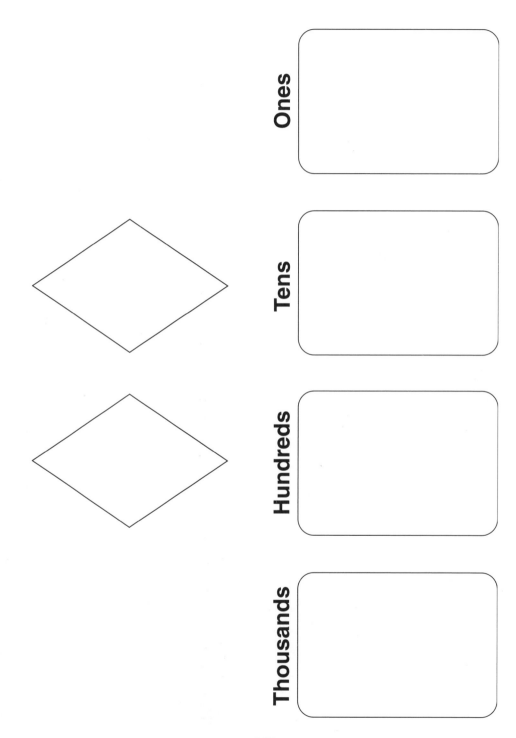

A TARGET ROUND VARIATION

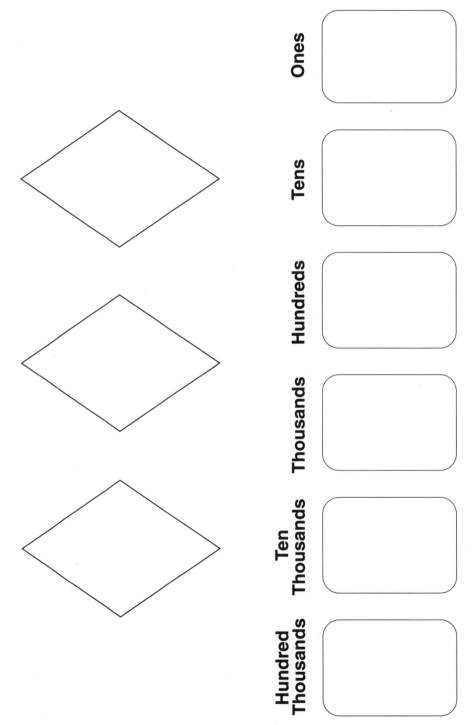

Ones

Tens

Hundreds

Thousands

Ten Thousands

Hundred Thousands

DRIVING RANGE

Guess Any Number	Does it fit the range?	Guess The Range	Is this the range?	Other Possibilities
1.				
2.				
3.				
4.				
5.				

ROLL A 100!

SCORING SYSTEM

2 decadice (80 + 20)	=	100	=	**2pts**
3 decadice (60 + 10 + 30)	=	100	=	**3pts**
2 separate decadice combos (40 + 60) (70 + 30)	=	100	=	**4pts**
4 decadice (10 + 20 + 60 + 10)	=	100	=	**6pts**

RECORD YOUR SUMS OF 100

1.	
2.	
3.	
4.	
5.	
6.	
7.	
8.	

TWO HUNDRED

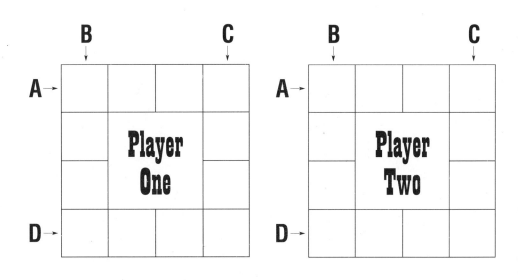

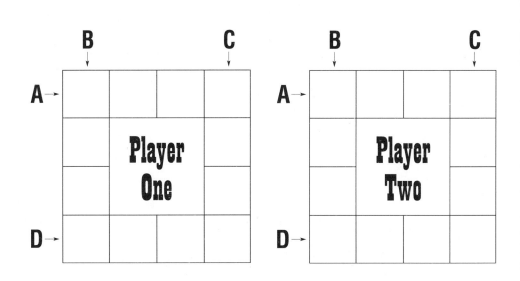

OUTCOME CHART FOR DECIDEDLY DIFFERENT

55 outcomes
19 are strikes

Difference = 0	Difference = 10	Difference = 20	Difference = 30	Difference = 40	Difference = 50	Difference = 60	Difference = 70	Difference = 80	Difference = 90
90 - 90	90 - 80	90 - 70	90 - 60	90 - 50	90 - 40	90 - 30	90 - 20	90 - 10	90 - 00
80 - 80	80 - 70	80 - 60	80 - 50	80 - 40	80 - 30	80 - 20	80 - 10	80 - 00	
70 - 70	70 - 60	70 - 50	70 - 40	70 - 30	70 - 20	70 - 10	70 - 00		
60 - 60	60 - 50	60 - 40	60 - 30	60 - 20	60 - 10	60 - 00			
50 - 50	50 - 40	50 - 30	50 - 20	50 - 10	50 - 00				
40 - 40	40 - 30	40 - 20	40 - 10	40 - 00					
30 - 30	30 - 20	30 - 10	30 - 00						
20 - 20	20 - 10	20 - 00							
10 - 10	10 - 00								
00 - 00									

DECA GOLF

1st Hole	2nd Hole	3rd Hole
4th Hole	5th Hole	6th Hole
7th Hole	8th Hole	9th Hole

SCORE PAD

	1st	2nd	3rd	4th	5th	6th	7th	8th	9th	Total Score

DESCRIBE YOUR GAME STATEGY

RED RACERS

FOOTBALL FACTOR

Player Two

	Touchdown	Field Goal	Total
1st Quarter			
2nd Quarter			
3rd Quarter			
4th Quarter			

Total Football Score

Player One

	Touchdown	Field Goal	Total
1st Quarter			
2nd Quarter			
3rd Quarter			
4th Quarter			

Total Football Score

Player Two

	Touchdown	Field Goal	Total
1st Quarter			
2nd Quarter			
3rd Quarter			
4th Quarter			

Total Football Score

Player One

	Touchdown	Field Goal	Total
1st Quarter			
2nd Quarter			
3rd Quarter			
4th Quarter			

Total Football Score

THE GREAT DIVIDE

ROLL	POINTS	ACCUMULATIVE TOTAL

GOT IT / CLOSEST TO!

	TARGET	NUMBER	EVALUATE
1			
2			
3			
4			
5			
6			
7			
8			
9			
10			

TARGET ZERO

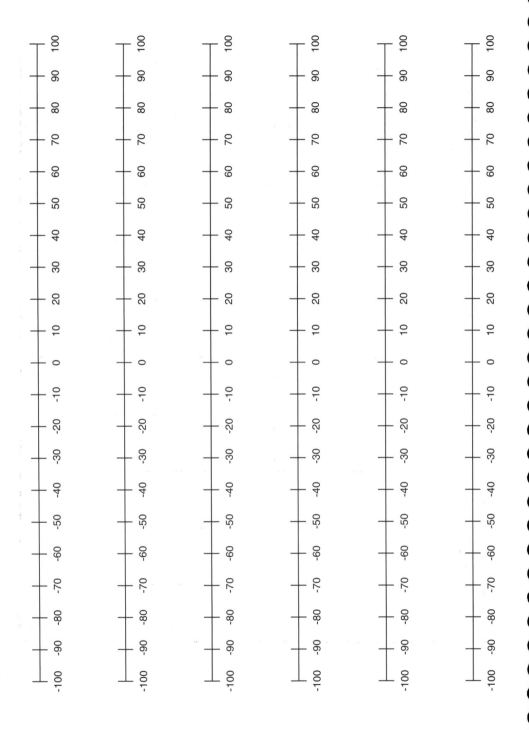

TARGET ZERO

-100 -90 -80 -70 -60 -50 -40 -30 -20 -10 0 10 20 30 40 50 60 70 80 90 100

Roll	My Math Sentence

DECI-DECA

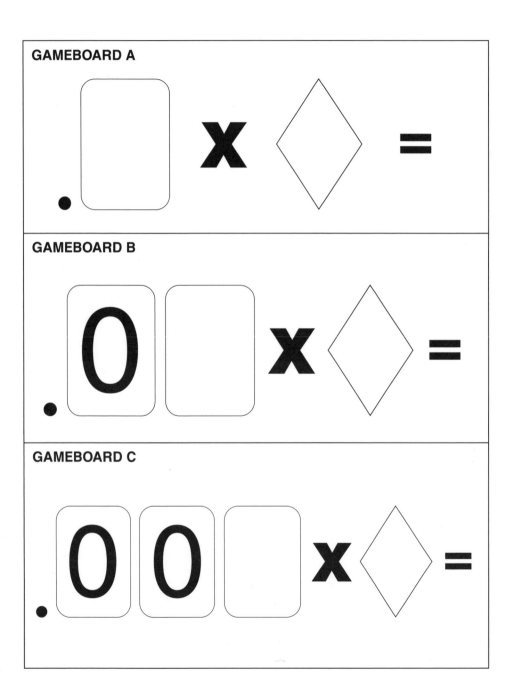

MILLIMETRE MAZE

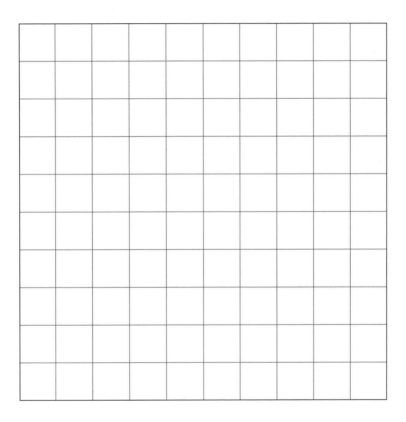

Appendix of Skills

box cars
and
one-eyed jacks®

About the Authors

The BOX CARS & ONE-EYED JACKS team of Joanne Currah and Jane Felling bring both innovation and inspiration to their consulting. They have combined expertise in elementary and special education and have conducted extensive research into the area of Games as a Teaching Strategy.

The authors developed all of the games for BOX CARS AND ONE-EYED JACKS Volume I "Shuffling Into Math" while teaching in their classrooms. Since the original publication in 1989, the authors have been successfully inservicing across Canada, the United States, Europe, Australia and Asia.

In 1991 BOX CARS won a National Award from the Learning Disabilities Association.

During 1992 BOX CARS Volume II "All Hands on Deck" and Volume III "Dice Works" were published to meet the growing demand by teachers and parents for new material. Their math books and manipulatives were intended for Kindergarten to Grade 7 and incorporated the use of cards, dice, and special ten, twelve, twenty, and thirty-sided dice. In 1994 "Money Matters for Kids" (Canadian Version) and "Rolling In The Dough" (American Version) Volumes IV and Volume V "Math Attack with 30-Sided Dice" were published. Volumes I, II, and III reached National Best Selling status in 1994!!

"On a Roll to Spelling", published in 1995 led the authors in a brand new direction with their games. Eagerly awaited by both teachers and parents, "On a Roll to Spelling" quickly became a favourite! This volume incorporated the use of alphabet dice and letter tiles and was designed to put the fun back into Spelling! Stratedice came next. Stratedice is a unique tray of 36 dice and gamebook. It also was published in 1995 and has reached Best Selling status.

In 1996 "Radical Math" Junior High and High School Games was published. The authors are pleased that their games and ideas are now extended across the grades.

"Piece it Together with Fractions" was completed in 1997. This games book comes with special fraction dice and manipulatives that make fractions fun and easy to understand. A new tactile spelling games book, "Spelling Rules... With These Cool Tools!" came next and was a great addition to the language games. Lastly, Decadice was completed in 2000. This games book is an author favourite as it includes numerous "Thought Provokers" to challenge game players of all ages.

box cars and one-eyed jacks®

2001 PRICE LIST

3930 - 78 Avenue, Edmonton, Alberta, Canada   T6B 2W4
Phone 1-780-440-MATH • Fax 1-780-440-1619
Website: boxcarsandoneeyedjacks.com
Email: boxcars@planet.eon.net

BOOKS

				QUANTITY	TOTAL
Shuffling Into Math Vol. I	☐	K-3	$21.95	_____	_____
All Hands On Deck Vol. II	☐	1-9	$21.95	_____	_____
Dice Works Vol. III (comes with 6 multi-sided dice)	☐	K-9	$23.95	_____	_____
Money Matters for Kids Vol. IV	☐	K-9	$21.95	_____	_____
Math Attack Vol. V (comes with 4 x 30-sided dice)	☐	K-9	$24.95	_____	_____
On a Roll to Spelling...and More Vol. VI (comes with 2 special alphabet dice)	☐	K-6	$22.95	_____	_____
Radical Math Vol. VII (comes with 10 multi-sided dice)	☐	7-12	$36.00	_____	_____
Piece It Together With Fractions Vol. VIII (comes with 7 fraction dice, one 12-sided number die, one mini deck of cards and a 51 pc. deluxe fraction set)	☐	1-9	$36.00	_____	_____
DecaDice Vol. IX (NEW) (comes with 4 decade dice and 4 x 10-sided dice)	☐	1-9	$26.95	_____	_____
Spelling Rules with These Cool Tools (comes with 2 special alphabet dice and a set of 60 alphabet tiles)	☐	K-7	$18.95	_____	_____
Box Cars and One-Eyed Jacks version française (comes with 6 multi-sided dice)	☐	K-9	$24.00	_____	_____

PLAYING CARDS

Special "Mini" Decks with 0, 1, 11, 12's	$2.50 each or 5 decks/$10.00		_____ _____
Special Large Floor Demonstration Deck (NEW) with 0, 1, 11, 12's - 7" x 4-3/4"		$12.00	_____ _____
Special Large Floor Demonstration Deck (NEW) with 0, 1, 11, 12's - 7" x 4-3/4"; plus Teaching Apron Set		$16.00	_____ _____
Regular Large Floor Demonstration Deck - 7" x 4-3/4"		$12.00	_____ _____
Regular Large Floor Demonstration Deck - 7" x 4-3/4" plus Teaching Apron Set		$16.00	_____ _____

OVERHEAD TRANSPARENCIES / MATERIALS

Set of Black & Red Overheads (includes 4 sheets = 84 cards total) Ace-King	$10.00	_____ _____
Set of Black & Red Overheads to Match Special Decks (with 0, 1, 11, 12's) (includes 4 sheets = 84 cards total)	$10.00	_____ _____
Money Overheads (includes 2 sheets of all coins - 133 total/ grey & copper)	$ 5.00	_____ _____
Alphabet Overheads (includes 3 sheets) - upper and lower case letter tiles & blends, etc.	$ 7.50	_____ _____
Deluxe Overhead Fraction Circles (51 pieces)	$12.00	_____ _____
Deluxe Overhead Alphabet Tiles (26 lowercase)	$7.95	_____ _____

DICE		QUANTITY	TOTAL
Regular Dice	5 / $1.00		
Manipulite Dice	$1.00 / pair, $10.00 / 12 pairs, $20.00 / 25 pairs, $27.00 / 36 pairs		
10-sided Spotted (0-9)	$ 1.00 / die		
10-sided Decade Dice (00, 10, 20...90)	$1.00 / die, $1.50 / pair		
10-sided (0-9)	$1.00 / die, $1.50 / pair		
12-sided (1-12)	$1.00 / die, $1.50 / pair		
20-sided (1-20)	$1.00 / die, $1.50 / pair		
10-sided Large Demo Decade Dice (00, 10, 20,... 90)	$2.00 / die, $3.00 / pair		
10-sided Large Demo Dice (0 - 9)	$2.00 / die, $3.00 / pair		
12-sided Large Demo Dice (1-12)	$2.00 / die, $3.00 / pair		
20-sided Large Demo Dice (1-20)	$2.00 / die, $3.00 / pair		
30-sided (1-30)	$2.00 / die, $3.00 / pair		
6-sided (0-5)	$1.00 / die, $1.50 / pair		
Operation (+ -)	$1.00 / die, $1.50 / pair		
Operation (+ - x ÷)	$1.00 / die, $1.50 / pair		
Fraction Dice	set of 7 / $5.00		
Large Coin Die	$5.00 / die		
Blank Dice	$0.75 / die, $1.00 / pair		
Overhead Spotted (1-6) Dice	$7.50 / pair		
Alphabet Dice (30-sided)	$2.50 / die, $4.00 / pair		
Large Floor Demo Dice	$4.50 / pair		
Overhead Fraction Dice	$7.50 / pair		
Overhead Numeral (1-6) Dice	$7.50 / pair		

KITS (see opposite page for descriptions)		QUANTITY	TOTAL
1. BASIC PRIMARY KIT	$ 65.95		
2. BASIC INTERMEDIATE KIT	$ 65.95		
3. RADICAL MATH KIT	$120.00		
4. DECADICE KIT *NEW KIT*	$ 49.95		
5. SPELLING KIT	$142.45		
6. MONEY MATTERS KIT	$ 70.95		
7. FRACTION KIT *NEW PRICE*	$147.00		
8. STRATEDICE CLASSROOM KIT	$145.00		
9. DELUXE PRIMARY K-4 KIT	$321.75		
10. DELUXE INTERMEDIATE 5-9 KIT	$319.75		
11. DELUXE FRACTION KIT *NEW PRICE*	$340.00		
12. SUPER SAVER KIT	$966.95		
13. CLASSROOM FUN "DIE" MENTALS (PRIMARY K-3)	$ 55.00		
14. CLASSROOM FUN "DIE" MENTALS (MIDDLE GRADES 4-9)	$ 64.50		
15. FRENCH FAVOURITES KIT	$ 94.00		

STRATEDICE

Gamebook, tray and 36 dice (revised '99)	1 - 9	$17.95	_____	_____
Tray and 36 dice (only)	1 - 9	$ 9.95	_____	_____
3 trays and 108 dice (comes with gamebook)	1 - 9	$31.95	_____	_____

MISCELLANEOUS

PUZZLE ISLAND (spelling-story book)	1 - 6	$12.00	_____	_____
ALPHA-DECK CARDS (2 decks)	K - 3	$ 9.95	_____	_____
ALPHA-DECK GAMES BOOK	K - 3	$12.95	_____	_____
ALPHA-DECK CARDS & BOOK SET	K - 3	$19.95	_____	_____
ALPHABET TILES 120 Upper case		$10.00 or 2/$15.00	_____	_____
120 Lower case		$10.00 or 2/$15.00	_____	_____
60 Blends & more		$10.00 or 2/$15.00	_____	_____
MONEY Canadian Coins		$10.50	_____	_____
- Plastic coins including pennies, nickels, dimes, quarters, loonies and twoonies (135 coins total)				
BINGO CHIPS Stock Colours (200/pkg.) $2.50 or 6/$12.00			_____	_____
MATH VELCRO PACK		$5.95 or 2/$10.00	_____	_____
(or $4.50 each for class sets of 30 or more)				
TEACHING APRON (holds Demo Deck)		$ 6.00	_____	_____
DELUXE DICE "COLLECTORS" PUZZLE				
500 pieces		$14.00	_____	_____
CLASSROOM SET OF 30 LARGE FLOOR DEMO DICE				
(indented dots only, not printed)		$45.00 / set	_____	_____
DELUXE FRACTION CIRCLES SET				
(51 pieces)		$12.00 or 2/$20.00	_____	_____
CALCULATOR–CASH REGISTER		$49.95	_____	_____
CALCULATOR–CASH REGISTER AND **MONEY MATTERS GAMES BOOK** SAVINGS		$67.95	_____	_____
MUG O' DICE (Coffee mug with 1 pair of large floor demo dice)		$ 4.95	_____	_____

                                                         SUBTOTAL _____

SHIPPING & HANDLING (use appropriate category)

OR	Orders under $100.00: (minimum shipping charge $5.00)	add 10% _____
OR	Orders under $500.00:	add 8% _____
	Orders over $500.00:	add 5% _____

                                                  SUBTOTAL _____

MINISTRY APPROVED RESOURCES

(#135980407) **HST 15%** (If Applicable) _____

or **GST 7%** _____

(PRICES SUBJECT TO CHANGE WITHOUT NOTICE)   **TOTAL** _____

Make cheques payable to: Box Cars & One-Eyed Jacks
Please allow 3 - 6 weeks for delivery

SEND TO: **P.O. # (if applicable)**_____

NAME _____

SCHOOL _____

STREET _____

CITY _____ PROVINCE _____

SCHOOL TELEPHONE _____ POSTAL CODE _____

HOME TELEPHONE _____ DATE _____

NEW IMPROVED KITS

1. BASIC PRIMARY KIT

SAVE $6⁵⁰

Shuffling Into Math Vol. I	$	21.95
50 Regular Dice	$	10.00
10 Decks of Special Mini Cards (0 - 12)	$	20.00
Special Large Floor Demonstration Deck plus Teaching Apron Set	$	16.00
Large Floor Demo Dice	$	4.50
Total Retail	$	72.45
Kit Price	**$**	**65.95**

2. BASIC INTERMEDIATE KIT

SAVE $6⁵⁰

All Hands On Deck Vol. II	$	21.95
50 Regular Dice	$	10.00
10 Decks of Special Mini Cards (0 - 12)	$	20.00
Card Overheads	$	10.00
Overhead Spotted Dice	$	7.50
Operations x 4	$	3.00
Total Retail	$	72.45
Kit Price	**$**	**65.95**

3. RADICAL MATH KIT

SAVE $8⁵⁰

Box Cars & One-Eyed Jacks Radical Math Vol. VII (with 10 multi-sided dice)	$	36.00
Overhead Cards	$	10.00
Overhead Spotted Dice	$	7.50
50 Regular Dice	$	10.00
10 Decks of Special Mini Cards (0 - 12)	$	20.00
Multi-Sided Dice:		
0-9 Numbers X 12	$	9.00
1-12 Numbers X 12	$	9.00
1-20 Numbers X 12	$	9.00
1-30 Numbers X 12	$	18.00
Total Retail	$	128.50
Kit Price	**$**	**120.00**

4. DECADICE KIT

SAVE $7⁰⁰

Decadice Vol. IX (with 8 multi-sided dice)	$	26.95
Multi-Sided Dice:		
0-9 Numbers x 16	$	12.00
00-90 Decade Dice x 16	$	12.00
10-sided Large Demo 0-9 Dice x 2	$	3.00
10-sided Large Demo Decade 00-90 Dice x 2	$	3.00
Total Retail	$	56.95
Kit Price	**$**	**49.95**

5. SPELLING KIT

BONUS!!

On a Roll to Spelling and More Vol. VI (with 2 alphabet dice)	$	22.95
Spelling Rules With These Cool Tools (book only)	$	12.00
14 Extra Alphabet Dice	$	28.00
8 Packages of Alphabet Tiles - set pricing... Includes 3 upper, 3 lower & 2 blend combo pkgs.	$	60.00
Alphabet Overheads (3 sheets)	$	7.50
Puzzle Island	$	12.00
Kit Price	**$**	**142.45**

RECEIVE ONE SET OF 24 REUSEABLE GAMES - $12.00 VALUE!

6. MONEY MATTERS KIT

BONUS!!

Money Matters Vol. IV	$	21.95
Money Overheads	$	5.00
3 Packages of Canadian Coins	$	31.50
Large Coin Die	$	5.00
Overhead Spotted Dice	$	7.50
Kit Price	**$**	**70.95**

RECEIVE ONE SET OF 6 REUSEABLE GAMES & ONE COIN ROLLER - $6.00 VALUE!

7. FRACTION KIT

NEW REDUCED PRICING

Piece It Together With Fractions Vol. VIII (with 7 fraction dice, one 12-sided number die, one mini deck of cards and a 51 pc. deluxe fraction set)	$	36.00
5 Sets of Deluxe Fraction Circles, Fraction Dice, Cards, 12-sided Dice	$	91.50
1 Deluxe Overhead Fraction Circle Set	$	12.00
Overhead Fraction Dice	$	7.50
Kit Price	**$**	**147.00**

RECEIVE A BONUS BAG OF FRACTION DICE - $10.00 VALUE!

8. STRATEDICE CLASSROOM KIT

SAVE $12²⁵

Gamebook, tray and 36 dice (revised '99)	$	17.95
14 trays and 504 dice	$	139.30
Total Retail	$	157.25
Kit Price	**$**	**145.00**

9. DELUXE PRIMARY K-4 KIT

Box Cars & One-Eyed Jacks Vol. I, II, III, IV, IX	$	116.75
Set of Card Overheads	$	10.00
Large Floor Demo Deck & Special Demo Deck	$	24.00
15 Decks of Special Mini Cards (0 - 12)	$	30.00
6 Packages of Bingo Chips	$	12.00
50 Regular Dice	$	10.00
Multi-Sided Dice:		
0-5 Dice x 20	$	15.00
0-9 Spotted x 20	$	20.00
0-9 Numbers x 20	$	15.00
1-12 Numbers x 20	$	15.00
1-20 Numbers x 20	$	15.00
00-90 Decade Dice x 20	$	15.00
1-30 Numbers x 10	$	15.00
Operations x 6	$	4.50
Large Floor Demo Dice	$	4.50
Kit Price	**$**	**321.75**

RECEIVE THREE SETS OF 12 REUSEABLE GAMES & TWO TEACHING APRONS - $30.00 VALUE!

10. DELUXE INTERMEDIATE 5-9 KIT

BONUS!!

Box Cars & One-Eyed Jacks Vol. II, III, IV, V, IX	$	119.75
Set of Card Overheads	$	10.00
15 Decks of Special Mini Cards (0 - 12)	$	30.00
6 Packages of Bingo Chips	$	12.00
50 Regular Dice	$	10.00
Overhead Spotted Dice	$	7.50
Multi-Sided Dice:		
0-9 Numbers x 30	$	22.50
1-12 Numbers x 30	$	22.50
1-20 Numbers x 30	$	22.50
1-30 Numbers x 24	$	36.00
00-90 Decade Dice x 20	$	15.00
Operations x 16	$	12.00
Kit Price	**$**	**319.75**

RECEIVE THREE SETS OF 12 REUSEABLE GAMES & TWO VELCRO MATH PACKS - $28.00 VALUE!

11. DELUXE FRACTION KIT

Piece It Together With Fractions Vol. VIII
    (with 7 fraction dice, one 12-sided
    number die, one mini deck of cards
    and a 51 pc. deluxe fraction set) . . . . . . $ 36.00
16 Sets of Deluxe Fraction Circles, Fraction Dice,
    Cards, 12-sided Dice . . . . $ 284.50
1 Deluxe Overhead Fraction Circle Set . . . . . $ 12.00
Overhead Fraction Dice . . . . $ 7.50
Kit Price . . . . **$ 340.00**

RECEIVE A BONUS BAG OF FRACTION DICE - $35.00 VALUE!

The Whole
"Kit & Kaboodle"
For Your School!
$70.00 Bonus & $65.00 Savings!
W O W ! ! !

12. SUPER SAVER KIT
MATH

Box Cars & One-Eyed Jacks Vol. I, II, III, IV, V, IX
    & version Française . . . . $ 165.70
Radical Math Vol. VII (with 10 special dice) . . . . $ 36.00
Piece It Together With Fractions Vol. VIII
    (comes with manipulatives) . . . . $ 36.00
2 Sets of Card Overheads . . . . $ 20.00
2 Pairs of Overhead Spotted Dice . . . . $ 15.00
Money Overheads . . . . $ 5.00
Large Coin Die . . . . $ 5.00
1 Special Large Demonstration Deck and 1 Regular
    Large Demonstration Deck
    plus 2 Teaching Aprons . . . . $ 32.00
3 Pairs of Large Floor Demo Dice . . . . $ 13.50
30 Decks of Special Mini Cards (0 - 12) . . . . $ 60.00
12 Packages of Bingo Chips . . . . $ 24.00
100 Regular Dice . . . . $ 20.00
Multi-Sided Dice:
    0-5 Dice X 30 . . . . $ 22.50
    0-9 Spotted x 30 . . . . $ 30.00
    0-9 Numbers x 30 . . . . $ 22.50
    1-12 Numbers x 30 . . . . $ 22.50
    1-20 Numbers x 30 . . . . $ 22.50
    00-90 Decade Dice x 30 . . . . $ 22.50
    1-30 Numbers x 30 . . . . $ 45.00
    Operations x 16 . . . . $ 12.00
    36 pairs Manipulite . . . . $ 27.00
Stratedice - 3 sets of 3 Trays/Books . . . . $ 95.85
3 Packages of Canadian Coins . . . . $ 31.50

SPELLING / LANGUAGE

On A Roll to Spelling and More
    Vol. VI (with 2 alphabet dice) . . . . $ 22.95
Spelling Rules With These Cool Tools (with two
    alphabet dice & a set of 60 alphabet tiles) $ 18.95
30 Alphabet Dice . . . . $ 60.00
14 Packages of Alphabet Tiles - set pricing...
    Includes 5 upper, 5 lower & 4 blend combo pkgs. $ 105.00
2 Sets of Alphabet Overheads (6 sheets) . . . . . . $ 15.00
2 Puzzle Islands . . . . $ 24.00
Total Retail . . . . $ 1031.95
Kit Price . . . . **$ 966.95**

RECEIVE FIVE SETS OF 1 VELCRO MATH PACK,
EACH CONTAINING 16 REUSEABLE GAMES - $69.75 VALUE!

13. CLASSROOM FUN "DIE" MENTALS PRIMARY K-3 DICE KIT

16 X 10-sided dice 0 - 9 . . . . $ 12.00
16 x 12-sided dice 1 - 12 . . . . $ 12.00
16 x 20-sided dice 1 - 20 . . . . $ 12.00
8 x 30-sided dice 1 - 30 . . . . $ 12.00
4 x 6-sided dice 0 - 5 . . . . $ 3.00
4 x 10-sided spotted dice . . . . $ 4.00
Kit Price . . . . **$ 55.00**

COMES IN A 'HANDY' CARRYING CASE WITH SOME GAME IDEAS

14. CLASSROOM FUN "DIE" MENTALS MIDDLE GRADES 4 - 9 DICE KIT

20 X 10-sided Dice 0 - 9 . . . . $ 15.00
20 x 12-sided Dice 1 - 12 . . . . $ 15.00
20 x 20-sided Dice 1 - 20 . . . . $ 15.00
10 x 30-sided Dice 1 - 30 . . . . $ 15.00
6 x Operation Dice (+,-,x,÷) . . . . $ 4.50
Kit Price . . . . **$ 64.50**

COMES IN A 'HANDY' CARRYING CASE WITH SOME GAME IDEAS

15. FRENCH FAVOURITES KIT

Box Cars & One-Eyed Jacks version Française . . . . $ 24.00
50 Regular Dice . . . . $ 10.00
10 Decks of Special Mini Cards (0 - 12) . . . . $ 20.00
Large Floor Demo Dice . . . . $ 4.50
Set of Card Overheads . . . . $ 10.00
Overhead Spotted Dice . . . . $ 7.50
Multi-Sided Dice:
    0-9 Numbers X 8 . . . . $ 6.00
    1-12 Numbers X 8 . . . . $ 6.00
    1-20 Numbers X 8 . . . . $ 6.00
Kit Price . . . . **$ 94.00**

RECEIVE FOUR SETS OF 4 REUSEABLE GAMES - $8.00 VALUE!

If Math Is A Game
You'll Want To Play With Us!!
Call 780-440-MATH for
Workshops At Your School!